FORESTRY COMMISSION BULLETIN
No. 55

Aspects of Thinning

PROCEEDINGS OF A MEETING OF PROJECT GROUP P4.02 "ECONOMICS
AND HARVESTING OF THINNING" OF THE INTERNATIONAL UNION OF FOREST
RESEARCH ORGANISATIONS, HELD IN EDINBURGH FROM 30th
SEPTEMBER UNTIL 2nd OCTOBER, 1974

Edited by
G. J. HAMILTON, M.Sc.
Forestry Commission

LONDON: HER MAJESTY'S STATIONERY OFFICE

ISBN 0 11 710147 8

CONTENTS

All diagrams were provided by the respective authors.

PART I

EDITOR'S PREFACE

This Bulletin contains the papers presented at a meeting of the International Union of Forest Research Organisations (IUFRO) Project Group P4.02 "Economics and Harvesting of Thinnings", held in Edinburgh from 30 September until 2 October 1974.

The Project Group is led by Professor Horst Kramer of the University of Gottingen, Federal Republic of Germany, and draws its members from research workers engaged in a wide range of disciplines. These include researchers principally concerned with the effects of thinning on yield, size-class distribution etc., engineers concerned with harvesting problems, and forest economists.

Regular meetings of the Project Group are held, sometimes in conjunction with associated IUFRO Subject or Project Groups, and on other occasions independently. Almost invariably these meetings are held in a different country on each occasion. The Edinburgh meeting was the first to be held by the Group in Britain.

In welcoming the delegates and setting the scene for the meeting, Mr George D. Holmes, Forestry Commissioner for Harvesting and Marketing and a member of the Executive Board of IUFRO, stressed the importance of thinning to British forestry, pointing out that thinning currently accounted for 55% of the total production from Forestry Commission woodlands. Mr Holmes also referred to the increasing scarcity of forest labour and the parallel trend towards increased mechanisation in harvesting operations, which raised the kind of problems which the Project Group was well fitted to help solve.

Papers were invited on various aspects of thinning. The first session (Papers 1–7) concerning mainly yield aspects of thinning, was chaired by Professor Joran Fries, Royal College of Forestry, Stockholm. The second session (Papers 8–10) chaired by Professor Harold E. Young, was devoted principally to the damage caused to sites and stands by harvesting operations. Mr Alastair A. Rowan, of the Forestry Commission's Harvesting and Marketing Division, chaired the final session, Papers 11–15, in which the main consideration was the harvesting operation.

The papers are given more or less in the order in which they were presented. The discussion attending each paper was recorded and a much shortened edited version of this is given immediately following the paper.

I wish to thank the Department of Forestry and Natural Resources, Edinburgh University, and in particular Dr Douglas C. Malcolm, for the use of a lecture theatre for the meeting and for the excellent facilities provided.

I should also like to thank Noreen Busby for assistance during the meeting, for preparing many of the diagrams for publication and for transcribing the tape recording of the discussions.

G. J. HAMILTON
Forestry Commission Research Station
Alice Holt Lodge
Wrecclesham
Farnham
Surrey

LIST OF PARTICIPANTS

AUSTRALIA
Mr H. Porter   Forestry Commission of New South Wales, 93–95 Clarence Street, SYDNEY, NSW 2000.

AUSTRIA
Mr H. Enk   Forstliche Bundesversuchsanstalt, A-1131 VIENNA.

CANADA
Mr R. B. Forster   Forest Economics Research Institute, Nicol Building, 331 Cooper Street, OTTAWA, Ontario.

DENMARK
Mr H. Bryndum   Danish Forest Experimental Station, Springforbirej 4, Springforbi, 2930 KLAMPENBORG.

Mr A. Jensen   Royal Veterinary & Agricultural College, Department of Forestry, Thorvaldsensdej 57, 1871 COPENHAGEN 5.

FINLAND
Professor J. Hämäläinen   The Finnish Forest Research Institute, Department of Forest Economics, Kaisaniemenkatu 1.A, 00100 HELSINKI 10.

FRANCE
Mr P. Guillon   Centre National de Recherches Forestières, Laboratoire d'Économie Forestière, 14 rue Girardet, 54042 NANCY.

GERMANY, Federal Republic of
Professor F. Franz   Forstliche Forschungsanstalt, D-8000 MUNCHEN 40, Amalienstrasse 52.

Professor H. Kramer   Institut für Forsteinrichtung und Ertragskunde der Universität Göttingen, 34 GÖTTINGEN, Busgenweg 5.

Mr Hans-Ulrich Sinner   D-8031 GROEBENZELL, Brennerstrasse 22.

Mr J. Stratmann   D-3282 Steinheim 2/Westfalen GREVENHAGEN In der Schwalge 1.

IRELAND, Republic of
Mr G. J. Gallagher   Department of Lands (Forest & Wildlife Service), Sidmonton Place, BRAY, Co. Wicklow.

Mr M. Swann   Department of Lands (Forest & Wildlife Service), 22 Upper Merrion Street, DUBLIN 2.

NETHERLANDS
Mr P. J. Faber   Growth & Yield Section, Forest Research Station, "De Dorschkamp", Postbus 23, WAGENINGEN.

NEW ZEALAND
Mr W. R. J. Sutton   Forest Research Institute, ROTORUA.

NORWAY
Mr Eivind Bauger   Norwegian Forest Research Institute, N-5047 STEND.

Professor Ola Børset   Norges Landbrukshogskole, Institutt för Skogskjøtsel, Boks 42 – 1432 VOLLEBEKK.

PAPUA NEW GUINEA
Dr J. E. D. Fox   Regional Forest Office, P O Box 267, MT HAGEN.

POLAND
Professor Tr Trampler   Forest Research Institute, Instuitut Badawczy Lesnictwa, ul. Wery Kostrzewy 3, WARSAW 22.

SOUTH AFRICA
Professor A. van Laar   Faculty of Forestry, University of Stellenbosch, STELLENBOSCH.

SWEDEN

Mr Carl J. Bredberg	Royal College of Forestry, S-770 73 GARPENBERG.
Professor Jöran Fries	Royal College of Forestry, S-104 05 STOCKHOLM 50.
Mr Hans Liedholm	Royal College of Forestry, S-770 73 GARPENBERG.

SWITZERLAND

Mr J. Ph. Schutz	Eidgenossisch Anstalt fur das Forstliche Versuchswesen, CH-8903 BIR-MENSDORF.

UNITED KINGDOM

Mr P. Adlard	Department of Forestry, Commonwealth Forestry Institute, South Parks Road, OXFORD.
Mr R. J. N. Busby	Forestry Commission, 231 Corstorphine Road, EDINBURGH.
Mr J. M. Christie	Forestry Commission, Forest Research Station, Alice Holt Lodge, FARNHAM, Surrey.
Mr J. Drummond	Forestry Commission, Stable Cottages, Mabie, DUMFRIES D92 8HB.
Mr G. J. Hamilton	Forestry Commission, Forest Research Station, Alice Holt Lodge, FARNHAM, Surrey.
Mr G. D. Holmes	Forestry Commission, 231 Corstorphine Road, EDINBURGH.
Mr G. M. Locke	Forestry Commission, 231 Corstorphine Road, EDINBURGH.
Mr R. F. MacKenzie	Forestry Division, Northern Ireland Department of Agriculture, Dundonald House, Upper Newtownards Road, BELFAST BT4 3SB.
Dr D. C. Malcolm	Department of Forestry & Natural Resources, Edinburgh University, Kings Buildings, Mayfield Road, EDINBURGH.
Mr A. A. Rowan	Forestry Commission, 231 Corstorphine Road, EDINBURGH.
Mr A. Sutton	Forestry Commission, 231 Corstorphine Road, EDINBURGH.

U.S.A.

Professor D. Edward Aulerich	Forest Engineering Department, Oregon State University, CORVALLIS, Oregon.
Professor H. A. Froehlich	School of Forestry, Oregon State University, CORVALLIS, Oregon.
Mr J. E. King	Weyerhaeuser Company, Forestry Research Centre, 505 North Pearl Street, CENTRALIA, Washington 98531.
Mr D. K. Lewis	(Weyerhaeuser Company), c/o Commonwealth Forestry Institute, South Parks Road, OXFORD OX1 3RB.
Mr M. Rowley	Forest Engineering Department, Oregon State University, CORVALLIS, Oregon, 97330, USA.
Mr J. E. Todd	Forest Service, USDA, Division of Timber Management, 14th & Independence Avenue, SW, WASHINGTON DC 20250.
Professor Harold E. Young	School of Forest Resources, University of Maine, ORONO, Maine 04473.

PART II

SUMMARIES OF PAPERS

PAPER 1

PRELIMINARY RESULTS FROM SOME NEW DANISH THINNING EXPERIMENTS WITH
NORWAY SPRUCE ON FERTILE SOILS

By H. BRYNDUM

This article reports preliminary results obtained from two recent thinning experiments in Norway spruce (*Picea abies*) on fertile soils in Denmark. Experiments were established in 1953 and 1960 respectively in young unthinned plantations with rather high stem numbers. The latest assessment is from 1973. The thinning treatments, controlled by basal area, are the following:

A, B, C, D, corresponding to no thinning, light thinning, medium heavy thinning and very heavy thinning, and D–B, very heavy thinning in youth with light thinning later.

In both experiments the volume increment was approximately the same in all treatments in the experimental periods of, respectively 20 and 13 years, with some extra increment in the heavier grades during the initial years. The height increment is not, or very little, influenced by the thinning, whereas the diameter increment rises steeply with increasing thinning intensity. The thinning intensity has a decisive influence on the dimensional composition of the total production. With increasing intensity there is an increasing shift of the volume production from the middle diameter classes into the higher classes.

The wood quality is somewhat reduced with increasing thinning intensity; the bole height becomes shorter; the taper more pronounced, and the branch diameter larger. It has not been possible to demonstrate any connection between thinning intensity and the frequency of rot. The risk of windthrow seems greater with increased thinning intensity, especially at greater stand heights. During the first years after the start of the heavy thinning operations there is an increased risk of snow damage in these treatments. Later when regular crowns have been formed the heavily thinned stands are very snow resistant.

Until now the heavy thinning grades have yielded by far the greatest net revenue. The total value production, ie the value of thinnings plus main crop at the respective ages at which data were collected, 34 and 38 years respectively, is greatest for the heaviest thinning grades. The same applies to capital value. Value production is still rising markedly with increasing age.

PAPER 2

EFFECTS OF LINE THINNING ON INCREMENT

By G. J. HAMILTON

The results from five experiments involving line thinning treatments show that:

a. A loss of production is associated with the neutral thinning type implicit in line thinning,
b. the zone of influence of line thinning is largely confined to the rows immediately adjacent to those removed,
c. the response of outside rows rises markedly as the number of adjacent rows removed increases, and
d. greater losses in volume production are associated with greater numbers of adjacent rows removed.

4

PAPER 3

DEVELOPMENT AND YIELD OF UNTHINNED NORWAY SPRUCE PLANTATIONS IN WEST NORWAY

By O. BØRSET

Investigations were made in 31 unthinned, densely planted plots of Norway spruce (*Picea abies*) in West Norway when the top height of most plots was in the region of 16–25 m. The plots were mainly on steep slopes in good positions and in a moist climate (annual rainfall 1500–3000 mm). Most of the stands were planted at spacings closer than $1 \cdot 5 \times 1 \cdot 5$ m.

The total production differed little from that of thinned stands. The volume loss due to natural mortality was always less than 10%. Dead trees appear to have been suppressed at an early stage and generally had died before reaching sawlog size. At a mean height of 15 m more than 80% of the volume was generally composed of trees having a breast height diameter of more than 11 cm. At a mean height of 20 m more than 80% of the volume consisted of trees with a breast height diameter above 17 cm. Health and stability were considered adequate.

The investigated, unthinned stands have developed better than was expected on the strength of experience with thinning experiments in other parts of northern regions. The explanation for this may be found in the advantageous water regime of the stands.

PAPER 4

THE DEVELOPMENT OF THINNING AND HARVESTING SYSTEMS IN YOUNG SITKA SPRUCE AND CONTORTA PINE CROPS

By G. J. GALLAGHER

Experimental evidence has shown that the removal of one-third of the standing volume at first thinning causes no great loss of volume increment in Sitka spruce (*Picea sitchensis*) and, somewhat less noticeably, in Contorta pine (*Pinus contorta*). A large number of different thinning methods of moderate degree appear to have little effect on volume production, although selective thinnings might be marginally superior. These results have led to the investigation of line thinnings in which each third or second row has been removed. These are the least expensive of the methods studied. These thinning methods have been tried in conjunction with different timber harvesting and extraction methods. The extraction of whole trees with large machines has not yet had as much success as simpler methods. The skyline systems are being developed for hilly areas. Contorta pine appears to be more sensitive to storm damage than Sitka spruce. After recent storms the damage done to Sitka spruce was much less than expected.

PAPER 5

NEW ZEALAND EXPERIENCE WITH RADIATA PINE

By W. R. J. SUTTON

Unthinned Radiata pine (*Pinus radiata*) plantations on long rotations incur serious risk of insect or disease attack. The first major attempt at commercial thinning failed to increase total yields or secure intermediate financial returns. This led to the development of an alternative regime giving similar volume yield, but economically and silviculturally superior. This regime incorporated wide initial spacing, heavy early thinning (without yield) and severe pruning.

PAPER 6

Thinning Research in South Africa

By A. VAN LAAR

In South Africa "Correlated Curve Trend Experiments" have been laid down to investigate the relationship between stand density and growth in even-aged forest stands. Each individual series comprises eight spacing plots with stem numbers varying between 125 and 3,000 per hectare. The experiment is combined with an assessment of the volume production of thinning plots which form part of the trial project. This allows the application of CCT growth series for the prognosis of growth in thinning plots. Total production, as well as other parameters of yield, were decisively influenced by stand density.

Additionally, thinning experiments have been laid down in *Pinus radiata* and *Populus deltoides* stands, either as completely randomised experimental plots or as blocks or split blocks, in the latter case in combination with thinning treatments. Because of the existence of reciprocal effects it is advisable to investigate simultaneously in twin factor experiments the influences of thinning and pruning on the growth of pine stands.

Thinning experiments in *Populus deltoides* stands demonstrated the superiority of using mean basal area as a measure of stand density. The experiments with *Pinus radiata* and *Populus deltoides* showed a curvilinear relationship between stand density and volume production. In order to assess competition within the plots thinned at varying degrees, competition variables were defined and correlated in the first place with the increment of individual trees. The relationship between these competition variables and increment was investigated using analysis of covariance.

PAPER 7

Growing Space Measurements – Complementary to Thinning Experiments

By A. M. JENSEN

In a 76-year old stand of Norway spruce (*Picea abies*) close to a thinning experiment, 247 single trees have been subjected to accurate measurements of the volume increment. Growing space has been measured and was calculated under different hypotheses of competition. The results from the single tree measurements are compared with the sample plot data from the thinning experiments. The use of growing space measurements is discussed.

PAPER 8

The Influence of Different Types of Thinning on Growth and Damage to Stands. Results of Experiments from Norway Spruce Stands in the German Federal Republic

By H. KRAMER

Maximising forest rents, which is the aim of Norway spruce (*Picea abies*) management in Central Europe, demands optimal increment and value and the avoidance of damage to stands. Wide spacing at stand establishment and an early reduction of stems raised the value increment and the resistance of a stand to snow and wind damage. To rationalise the thinning of closely spaced Norway spruce stands, crown, line and strip thinning are recommended as well as combinations of these thinning methods. The effects of systematic thinning on increment and damage to stands are examined. A comparison of low thinning, crown thinning and strip thinning (Table 8.1) shows that low thinning does extremely badly from the economic point of view. Crown and strip thinning are roughly equally advantageous. According to the increment analysis (Table 8.2) low thinning and crown thinning produce practically the same volume increment. The five year volume increment of the line thinning is 8% lower than the low thinning but is barely noticeable (at 0·6%) in a rotation period of 100 years. The increment of the 400 trees of largest diameter (elite trees) in line thinning is 5% greater than with low thinnings and with crown thinning 14% greater. Early heavy thinning encourages crown development (Table 8·3) especially with crown thinning.

With extreme line thinning (removal of every 4th line in a stand with 3 m spacings between lines) with thinning strips of 6 m width, no definite loss of increment (mean 3%) could be shown as against selective low thinning (Table 8.4).

A stand of Norway spruce in the Harz Mountains currently 100 years old in which two-thirds of the volume was removed 45 years ago by felling every second and third line shows very considerable volume and value production (Table 8.5).

A special "Caterpillar" tractor was used for the mechanical reduction of stands in extremely dense spruce stands of some 8 m in height. Strips of 2·5 m in width and at intervals of 8 m were cut and flattened. This operation was extremely cheap and no damage occurred in consequence.

Where a short wood method (production of wood for industry 2 m in length, with bark) was employed, three different types of strip thinnings were tested. The strip width in each case was 4·5 m while the distance between the edges of the strips varied from 3–15 m. Except in the case of the closest strip, the strip thinning was combined with crown thinning in the areas between strips. The best performance was in pure strip thinning at close intervals. But this was accompanied also by the greatest damage to the trees. Soil and root damage is avoided by means of brushwood covering the strips.

The use of the whole tree harvesting method causes, among other things, greater damage especially to the base of the tree than the shortwood method of harvesting.

Wind damage occurs especially in older Norway spruce stands. Heavier thinning operations in young stands, including line and strip thinning, enabled the stands to survive the storm catastrophe of November 1972.

Snow breakage on the other hand endangers the younger stands particularly. The percentage of loss from snow rises in proportion to the relationship between height and diameter, and inversely with the crown percentage (see Figs 8.1 and 8.2). Within a stand, snow breakage decreases clearly with increasing diameter (Fig 8.3). Snow damage after strip and line thinning depends upon the condition of the stand and the period of time between thinning and the occurrence of damage. The stand is most vulnerable immediately after thinning. Damage occurring after systematic thinning is unimportant as only the weak trees are affected, which would already have been removed in low thinning (see Fig 8.4).

PAPER 9

VIEWS ON THE CHOICE OF SILVICULTURAL METHODS AND LOGGING TECHNIQUES IN THINNINGS

By JÖRAN FRIES

Damage caused by heavy vehicles in thinnings has been investigated. Damage to soil and roots increases rapidly when the bearing capacity of the ground decreases. Slash from felled trees on the haul-roads reduces damage substantially. Damage to roots of Norway spruce greater than 2 cm in diameter gives rise to rot infections which, if the damage is situated close to the tree (less than 0·5 m), in most cases will cause rot infection also in the stem. Damage to Scots pine seldom causes rot infection. One example is given of how simulation can be used to find the best combination of silvicultural method and logging technique.

PAPER 10

THE INFLUENCE OF DIFFERENT THINNING SYSTEMS ON DAMAGE TO SOIL AND TREES

By HENRY A. FROEHLICH

The concern about potential soil and tree damage due to thinning is increasing with increasing mechanisation. The actual growth losses to residual trees, or seedlings after the final cut, is not yet well defined. Highly variable results have been reported from thinning studies. These results vary as a result of differences in site factors, stand factors and operational factors. A general concept of the inter-relationship of these factors is given. Soil texture and soil moisture at time of thinning are the major items affecting soil compaction. Trafficability of soils as affected by litter or slashings have also been cited as causing differences in soil and tree damage. Tree species differ markedly in their susceptibility to damage from soil compaction, root breakage or stem wounds.

Soil and tree damage due to different thinning systems cannot be completely separated from the site and stand factors. The major difference in the impact of various thinning systems is apparently due to ground pressure and intensity or frequency of use. A study in thinning a 35-year old Douglas fir (*Pseudotsuga menziesii*) stand by both skyline and crawler tractor shows a large difference in extent of soil disturbance and soil compaction. Relatively little difference was observed in percent of stems with wounds. Tree wounds created by tractor thinning were generally near ground level and possibly subject to a higher incidence of rot infection than skyline wounds.

Much research is needed to make it possible to predict actual gross losses produced by the visible soil and stem damage.

PAPER 11

The Machines are Coming, The Machines are Coming

By HAROLD E. YOUNG

The successful adaptation of the mobile Chiparvestor developed by Morbark Industries, Inc. as a major component of a mechanical forest harvesting system and the equally successful industrial use of chips with bark attached by Mills Manufacturing Reconstituted Products has ushered in a whole new era in harvesting and use of primary forest products.

This highly lucrative market has encouraged a number of equipment companies to design mobile and self-propelled machines of various sizes to be used in both clear cutting and thinning operations. Many foresters are concerned that the use of such machines will result in overcutting and damage to the forest. Both are possible but unlikely as we adapt to and control the machines that will be at our disposal.

Mechanised harvesting is a response to the shortage of woods labour. Despite the high cost of the machines there is a decrease in the cost of wood delivered to the mills. Furthermore it is anticipated that in time there will be no such thing as a "pre-commercial" thinning which will mean that professional foresters will be able to manipulate the forest to control species, density and quality at no cost, and sometimes at a profit.

PAPER 12

The Technique of Thinning – The Problem and Means of Developing Sound Forest Management

By S. HÄBERLE

The technique of thinning must be directed to three targets:
  – A long term target which aims at achieving at rotation age, plots fully stocked with trees of the greatest possible value and dimensions
  – A medium term target which is devoted to making the stand accessible
  – A short term target which takes account of the profitability of current wood harvesting methods.

An attempt is made to demonstrate working techniques for the entire range of Norway spruce (*Picea abies*) thinnings, from young pole timber to old timber, which take these three targets into account in the best possible combination.

The following principles apply:
  The younger the stand the earlier systematic thinnings are permissible. These are accomplished with the help of a thinning and harvesting machine which can create strips of 4–5 m in width and which carries out the following processes; cutting, de-limbing, bucking, bunching, depositing in the strip.
The strips are 20–30 m apart. In the areas between strips a selective thinning is carried out. In the younger

stands shortwood is produced in 2 m standard lengths, while in middle-aged and older stands long timber is preferred.

With old timber the SERIAS-system is employed, whereby the trees to be harvested are branched and barked when standing. This system enables selective thinning operations to be carried out with no damage to the stem.

Should it not be possible to sell the removed trees profitably due to the unfavourable relationship between timber prices and felling costs, the final crop trees can be promoted by destroying their oppressors with the arboricide cartridges developed by Dr Sterzik. This method is permissible only when there is no danger from insects. Otherwise mechanical operations cannot be avoided even when there is a loss in the short run, for the long term aim in a cultivated forest demands thinning operations independent of the price/cost situation operating at that time.

PAPER 13

Thinning: The state of the Art in the Pacific Northwest

By D. E. AULERICH

Thinning in the Douglas fir (*Pseudotsuga menziesii*) forests of the Pacific Northwest is becoming a more frequent practice as many young stands replace old growth. Although the largest proportion of ongrowing operations are by ground based behicles, crawler tractors and rubber-tyred skidders, the interest in cable thinning is increasing. This is due primarily to the steep terrain and fragile soils characteristic of much of the region.

Major problems facing the operator are adapting workers to smallwood harvesting and obtaining equipment designed for handling smallwood.

Smallwood handling problems associated with the machine and system are being identified. This information will aid in the development of future equipment and techniques for harvesting, primarily yarding smallwood on steep, inaccessible terrain.

PAPER 14

Problems of Extraction of Thinnings by Cable-Crane in the United Kingdom

By J. A. DRUMMOND

Cable-cranes as used in the United Kingdom are of the short/medium range variety. They are sensitive in sky-line form to the yield produced from thinning especially in earlier stages.

Damage to soil and crop is very limited and there is little indication of instability from wind resulting from the layouts used.

PAPER 15

Mechanised Thinning Systems

By CARL-J. BREDBERG

Rapidly rising costs in thinnings have led to a reduction of thinning activities. If thinning is considered a necessary tool in the future treatment of stands we have to develop new logging machines and systems especially designed for high productivity and low costs in smallwood. The principle of handling bundles of small trees offers some promising solutions. However, a serious obstacle to mechanisation is the damage to the stand caused primarily by the terrain-transportation vehicles. An expensive and time-consuming development is required to solve this problem. Alternatively, we have to sacrifice the possibilities of using thinning as an aid in future forest management.

RESUMÉ DES COMMUNICATIONS

EXPOSÉ 1

Résultats Préliminaires de Certaines Nouvelles Expériences Danoises D'éclaircissage des Épicéas dans les Sols Fertiles

Par H. BRYNDUM

La communication publie des résultats préliminaires de deux essais d'éclaircies d'épicéa (*Picea abies*) sur sols riches au Danemark. Les deux essais ont été établis respectivement en 1953 et 1960 dans des jeunes peuplements assez denses, qui jusque-là n'ont jamais été touchés par la hache. Le dernier relevé date de 1973. Les degrés d'intensité d'éclaircies, étalonnés par la surface terrière, sont les suivants:

A, B, C, D et D–B, correspondants à des éclaircies naturelles (témoin), faibles, moyennes, très fortes et enfin très fortes dans la jeunesse suivies des interventions faibles.

Pendant la période d'observation de 20 et 13 ans respectivement, l'accroissement en volume des deux essais ne semble pas sensiblement influencé par la régime d'éclaircies. Seulement une legère stimulation de l'accroissement fût constatée dans les intensitées fortes dans les premières années. L'accroissement en hauteur est peu correllé avec l'intensité d'éclaircie, par contre l'accroissement en diamètre est fortement accéléré par les éclaircies fortes. Ainsi le régime d'éclaircie a eu une influence importante sur la proportion de bois fort dans la production totale, donnant de plus en plus de grandes dimensions avec des intensités croissantes. La qualité du bois d'oeuvre diminue un peu en conséquence d'un développement plus fort des cimes et des branches, ainsi que d'une décroissance métrique plus élevée, dans les fortes intensités.

Les risques de chablis semblent plus grands dans les intensités fortes, ce phénomène est surtout prononcé après une certaine hauteur des peuplements. Dans les jeunes âges les risques de dégats de neige semblent liés aux fortes réductions de tiges. Plus tard, quand les cimes se sont harmonisés, les faibles intensités d'éclaircies sont par contre les plus sensibles.

Les éclaircies fortes ont jusqu'à maintenant donné les revenus nets de loin les plus élevés. Il va de même pour la valeur de la production totale (éclaircies+peuplement sur pied). Aussi les bénéfices actualisés sont plus élevés dans les degrés d'intensités d'éclaircies fortes.

EXPOSÉ 2

Effets de L'éclaircissage en Ligne sur L'accroissement

Par G. J. HAMILTON

Les résultats de cinq expériences concernant l'éclaircie en ligne sont présentés. Ils indiquent:

   a. qu'il y a une réduction de production totale en volume qui s'est associée avec l'éclaircie neutre, ce qui est soi-même implicite par l'éclaircie en ligne
   b. que la zone d'influence sur l'éclaircie en ligne est largement limitée aux lignes absolument contigues aux lignes abbattues
   c. que la réaction des lignes extérieures augmente d'une façon marquée à l'égard de l'augmentation du nombre de lignes contigues qui sont abattues, et
   d. que plus les lignes avoisantes sont abattues, plus augmentent en volume les pertes de production.

EXPOSÉ 3

Développement et Rendement des Plantations D'épicéas Non Éclaircies en Norvège Occidentale

Par O. BØRSET

On a procédé en Norvège occidentale à des études sur 31 parcelles de terrain couvertes d'épaisses forêts d'épicéas (*Picea abies*) non éclaircies alors que l'étage dominant des arbres de la plupart de ces parcelles était de l'ordre de 16 à 25 m. Ces parcelles se trouvaient essentiellement sur des pentes abruptes, bien exposéees et dans un climat humide (quantité de pluie annuelle de 1500 à 3000 mm). La plupart des arbres sur pied étaient plantés à des intervalles inférieurs à $1·50 \times 1·50$ m.

La production totale s'est trouvé être sensiblement la même que celle des arbres sur pied ayant subi des opérations d'éclaircies. Les pertes découlant de la mortalité naturelle ont toujours été inférieures à 10%. Il semble que les arbres morts aient été supprimés dès les premiers stades et que dans l'ensemble ils soient morts avant d'avoir atteint la dimension voulue pour le bloc de sciage. A la hauteur moyenne de 15 m, plus de 80% du volume étaient généralement composés d'arbres ayant un diamètre supérieur à 11 cm, à hauteur de poitrine. A la hauteur moyenne de 20 m, plus de 80% du volume se composaient d'arbres ayant un diamètre supérieur à 17 cm, à hauteur de poitrine. On a considéré leur santé et leur stabilité comme étant adéquate.

Les parcelles de terrain non éclaircies que l'on a considérées se sont mieux développées qu'on ne l'avait anticipé à la lumière des résultats obtenus avec les expériences d'éclaircissage effectuées dans les autres parties des régions septentrionales. L'explication de cet état de choses peut se trouver dans le régime favorable des eaux de la parcelle de terrain.

EXPOSÉ 4

DÉVELOPPEMENT DES SYSTÈMES D'ÉCLAIRCISSAGE DES CULTURES DE JEUNES ÉPICÉAS SITKA ET DE PINS CONTORTA

Par G. J. Gallagher

Des expérimentations sur le degré d'intensité d'éclaircie suggèrent que l'enlèvement d'une troisième de la mètre cube mesurée au compas forestière de *Picea sitchensis* à la première éclaircie, et bien que moins sûr chez le *Pinus contorta*, ne donne pas de grandes pertes d'accroissement. Des éclaircies suivantes chez *Picea sitchensis* de 40–60% d'accroissement périodiques de la surface terrière, ou moins de 40% d'accroissement de contenance au volume doivent permettre la maintenance d'accroissement. Un grand nombre de façons différentes d'éclaircir d'intensité assez importante semblent d'avoir un effet peu considerable sur le rendement au volume, bien que l'éclaircie jardinée puisse être un peu meilleur. Ces résultats ont engendré des études sur d'éclaircie en lignes. Ce sont les méthodes les moins chères que l'on a examinees. Ces poids et ces façons d'éclaircir ont été essayés avec de diverses moyens de récolte et videnage de bois. La récolte d'arbres entiers avec les grandes machines n'a pas encore eu autant de succès que les méthodes plus simples avec les tracteurs. On développe des systèmes de câble suspendu pour les terrains accidentés. *Pinus cortorta* qui a été éclaircie se montre plus sensible au dégât d'ouragon que la *Picea sitchensis*. Le dégât d'ouragon *P. sitchensis*, éclaircie en lignes, a été beaucoup moins que l'on aurait cru.

EXPOSÉ 5

EXPÉRIENCE NÉO-ZÉLANDAISE SUR LE PIN RADIATA

Par W. R. J. SUTTON

Dans les plantations de *Pinus radiata* à longue révolution qui n'ont jamais été soumises aux éclaircies, il y a des risques sérieux d'attaque par les insectes ou par les maladies cryptogamiques. Le premier essai à faire des éclaircies commerciaux n'a pas réussi à augmenter les rendements en bois ou d'assurer des rendements intermédiaires en argent. Par conséquent, on a développé un régime alternatif qui donne des rendements pareils en volume mais qui possède une supériorité économique et culturelle. Ce régime comprend un écartement large, des éclaircies fortes et précoces (sans utilisation du matériel) et des élagages sévères.

EXPOSÉ 6

RECHERCHE SUR L'ÉCLAIRCISSAGE EN AFRIQUE DU SUD

Par A. VAN LAAR

En Afrique du Sud, on a spécifié des "expériences sur la tendance des courbes corrélatives" de manière à pouvoir étudier la relation qui existe entre la densité des parcelles de terrain et la croissance dans les parcelles de futaie régulière. Chaque série comporte huit parcelles d'espacement où le nombre des arbres varie entre 125 et 3.000 unités à l'hectare. Cette expérience est combineé avec une évaluation du volume de la production des parcelles d'éclaircissage qui font partie des essais. Cela permet l'application des séries de croissance à la tendance des courbes corrélatives pour faire des pronostics sur la croissance des parcelles d'éclaircissage. La production totale, ainsi que les autres paramètres de rendement, ont définitivement été influencés par la densité des arbres sur pied.

On a, de plus, spécifié des expériences d'éclaircissage pour les *Pinus radiata* et les *Populus deltoides* sur pied, soit en tant que parcelles expérimentales choisies au hasard ou en tant que blocs ou parties de blocs, et dans ce dernier cas en les combinant avec des opérations d'éclaircissage. En raison de l'existence d'effets réciproques, il est recommandé d'étudier simultanément, par des expériences à facteur jumelé, l'influence de l'éclaircissage et de l'émondage sur la croissance des pins sur pied.

Les expériences d'éclaircissage effectuées sur les *Populus deltoides* sur pied ont démontré la supériorité de l'utilisation d'une surface basale moyenne en tant que mesure de densité des arbres sur pied. Les expériences effectuées avec les *Pinus radiata* et les *Populus deltoides* ont montré une relation curviligne entre la densité des arbres sur pied et le volume de la production. Pour pouvoir évaluer la concurrence au sein des parcelles éclaircies à des degrés différents, les éléments variables de concurrence ont été définis et sont en premier lieu en corrélation avec l'accroissement de chaque arbre. La relation qui existe entre ces éléments variables de concurrence et l'accroissement a été étudiée grâce aux analyses de covariation.

EXPOSÉ 7

MESURE DE L'ESPACE VITAL – COMPLÉMENT DES EXPÉRIENCES D'ÉCLAIRCISSAGE

Par A. M. JENSEN

Dans un peuplement d'épicéa, (*Picea abies*) âgé de 76 ans, et situé à 1·5 km d'un dispositif expérimental d'éclarcie, 247 arbres individuels ont été sujet des mesures de précision d'accroissement en volume. L'espace productif de chaque arbre a été mesuré et calculé avec différents hypothèses de concurrence. Les resultats des mesures sur des arbres individuels sont comparés avec les données des placettes d'expériences de l'essai d'éclarcie. L'application des mesures de l'espace productif d'arbres individuels est finalement discutée.

EXPOSÉ 8

INFLUENCE DE DIFFÉRENTS TYPES D'ÉCLAIRCIES SUR LA CROISSANCE ET LES DOMMAGES AU PEUPLEMENT. RÉSULTATS DE RECHERCHES SUR L'ÉPICÉA DANS LA RÉPUBLIQUE D'ALLEMAGNE FÉDÉRALE

Par H. KRAMER

Le but matériel de l'économie de l'épicéa (*Picea abies*) en Europe centrale est l'obtention d'une rente forestière maximale. En vue d'atteindre ce but il est indispensable d'assurer un accroissement optimal en volume et en valeur et d'éviter les dommages aux peuplements. Un grand écartement des rangées de plantes à la création du peuplement et la réduction du nombre d'arbres dans la jeunesse font augmenter l'accroissement de valeur et la résistance à la cassure du peuplement causée par la neige et le vent. Il est recommandé d'effectuer des éclaircies en bouquets d'arbres, en lignes ou en tranchées aussi bien que des combinaisons de ces types d'éclaircies. Les effets des coupes schématiques sur l'accroissement et les dommages au peuplement ont été examinés. Une comparaison des 3 différents types d'éclaircies, à savoir l'éclaircie par le bas, l'éclaircie par le haut et l'éclaircie en lignes montre que, du point de vue économique, les résultats de l'éclaircie par le bas sont extrêmement mauvais (tableau 8.1). Les résultats de l'éclaircie par le haut et de l'éclaircie en lignes sont favorables et à peu près égaux. D'après l'analyse d'accroissement (Tableau 8.2) l'éclaircie par le bas et l'éclaircie par le haut fournissent à peu près même accroissement en volume. L'accroissement en volume dans les 5 premières années est inférieur de 8%, mais cette différence n'est que de 0·6% si on considère une période de révolution de 100 ans, et est par conséquent insignifiante.

L'accroissement des 400 arbres les plus forts=arbres d'avenir est pour l'éclaircie en lignes de 5%, pour l'éclaircie par le haut de 14% supérieur à l'accroissement sous le régime d'éclaircies par le bas. L'éclaircie forte dans les premières années et particulièrement l'éclaircie par le haut a stimulé le developpement de la couronne.

Une éclaircie en ligne extremement forte (élimination de chaque 4^{ieme} ligne d'arbres dans un peuplement établi à un écartement des lignes de 3 m) dans un peuplement à Briton n'a pas montré d'accroissement significatif (en moyenne 3%) en comparaison avec l'éclaircie individuelle.

Dans un peuplement du Harz qui avait subi 45 ans auparavant une forte réduction du volume total par l'élimination de chaque 2^{ieme} ou 3^{ieme} ligne, on a pu constater une très grande augmentation du volume et de la production de valeur.

La réduction du nombre d'arbres dans les peuplements jeunes très denses à été effectuée a l'aide d'un caterpillar spécial qui coupait à 8 m d'intervalle des coulisses de 2 m 50 de largeur. Ce procédé de travail est trés bon marché et les dommages au reste du peuplement sont pratiquement inexistants.

A la première éclaircie, où une methode de coupe en bris court a été employée (bois d'industrie avec écorce d'une longueur de 2 m, 3 différents procédés d'éclaircies en tranchées ont été examinés. La largeur des coulisses était de 4 m 50 et l'écartement entre deux coulisses variait entre 3 m et 15 m. A l'exception du plus petit écartement le procédé d'élimination schématique d'arbres a été combiné avec une éclaircie de sélection d'arbres dans les entrelignes. L'éclaircie en tranchées avec un écartement étroit des coulisses a produit le plus grand accroissement en volume, en même temps de très forts dommages ont été causés aux arbres restants. Aucun dommage au sol et aux racines n'a eu lieu à cause de la couverture de brindilles existantes. La méthode de coupe en bois long cause plus de dommages (particulièrement à l'empattement des arbres) que le procédé de coupe en bois court.

Les dégâts causés par le vent sont particulièrement fréquents dans les peuplements âgés. Les jeunes peuplements qui avaient reçu un traitement d'éclaircie forte, également ceux qui ont été l'objet d'éclaircie en lignes et en tranchées ont bien supporté l'ouragan de novembre 1972. En ce qui concerne les bris de neige les jeunes peuplements d'épicéa sont les plus menacés. Le pourcentage des abres endommagés augmente proportionnellement au rapport (hauteur/diamètre) et est inversement proportionnel au pourcentage de couronnes (voir graphiques 8.1 et 8.2). A l'intérieur du peuplement les bris de neige diminuent sensiblement avec l'augmentation du diamètre des arbres. Les expériences concernant les dommages causés par la neige aux peuplements éclaircis en lignes ou en tranchées sont différentes, dépendant de l'état du peuplement et de l'espace de temps entre l'éclaircie et l'apparition des dommages. La période de plus grand danger du peuplement se situe immédiatement après l'éclaircie. Les dommages causés après une éclaircie schématique sont pratiquement sans importance, car les arbres touchés sont le plus souvent ceux qui normalement seraient éliminés par une éclaircie par le bas.

EXPOSÉ 9

POINTS DE VUE SUR LE CHOIX DES MÉTHODES DE SYLVICULTURE ET DES TECHNIQUES D'ABATTAGE DANS LES OPÉRATIONS D'ÉCLAIRCIES

Par JÖRAN FRIES

On a effectué des études pour évaluer les dégâts causés au cours des opérations d'éclaircies par les véhicules lourds. Les dégâts infligés au sol et aux racines augmentent rapidement lorsque la capacité porteuse du sol diminue. Les déchets provenant des arbres abattus réduisent d'une manière substantielle les dégâts sur les routes de traction. Les dégâts aux racines des épicéas ayant plus de 2 cm de diamètre peuvent causer des infections putrides, lesquelles provoqueront, si elles se trouvent situées à proximité de l'arbre (moins de 0·50 m), une infection du tronc même de l'arbre. Les dégâts infligés au pin d'Ecosse provoquent rarement une infection putride. On donne un exemple de la manière dont on peut utiliser la simulation pour trouver une meilleure combinaison des méthodes de sylviculture et des techniques d'abattage.

EXPOSÉ 10

INFLUENCE DES DIFFÉRENTS SYSTÈMES D'ÉCLAIRCIE SUR LA DÉTÉRIORATION DU SOL ET DES ARBRES

Par H. A. FROEHLICH

La détérioration du sol et des arbres causée par la technique d'éclaircie est un sujet d'inquiètude grandissant avec le développement de la mécanisation. Les pertes effectives des arbres restant ou des nouvelles pousses après la coupe ne sont pas encore bien définies. Des résultats très variables ont été rapportés dans les études d'éclaircie. La variation des résultats est due aux différences dans le facteur de site, le facteur de position et le facteur opérationnel. Il est exposé un concept général d'interrelation de ces facteurs. La nature et l'humidité du sol au moment de l'opération d'éclaircie sont les facteurs principaux qui affectent la compacité du sol. La perturbation des sols par les chutes et coupures a aussi été mentionnée comme la cause de détérioration du sol et des arbres. Les arbres par leur espèce différent dans leur réponse à la détérioration due à la compacité du sol, aux racines brisées, ou aux blessures du tronc.

La détérioration du sol et de l'arbre due aux différentes techniques d'éclaircie ne peut pas être complètement séparée des facteurs de site et de position. La différence principale dans l'impact des différents systèmes d'éclaircie est apparemment due à la pression du sol et à l'intensité et à la fréquence de l'opération.

Une étude d'éclaircie d'un bois de pins Douglas (*Pseudotsuga menziesii*) âgés de 35 ans par un tracteur opérant en l'air et au sol montre une grande différence dans l'étendue de la détérioration du sol et de sa compacité. Relativement peu de différence a été observée dans le pourcentage de troncs endommagés. Les blessures des arbres causées par éclaircie au tracteur avaient lieu généralement près du niveau du sol et étaient plus souvent sujets au pourrissement qu'à des blessures de la cime.

De plus amples recherches sont nécessaires pour qu'il soit possible de prédire les pertes effectives dans la croissance des arbres dues à une détérioration visible du sol et du tronc.

EXPOSÉ 11

Voilà les Machines qui Arrivent, les Voilà qui Arrivent

Par HAROLD E. YOUNG

L'heureuse adaptation du Chiparvestor mobile réalisé par les Industries Morbark, Inc. en tant que composant majeur d'un système mécanisé d'exploitation des forêts et l'emploi tout aussi heureux de copeaux encore non séparés de l'écorce par des usines fabriquant des produits reconstitués nous a fait entrer dans une nouvelle ère en ce qui concerne la récolte et l'emploi des produits principaux de la forêt. Le marché extrêmement lucratif a encouragé un certain nombre de compagnies d'équipement à créer des machines de diverses tailles, mobiles et automotrices, destinées à servir à la fois à couper simplement et à ménager des éclaircies. Beaucoup de gens qui s'occupent de sylviculture s'inquiètent de ce que l'emploi de telles machines puisse avoir pour résultat de pratiquer des coupes excessives et d'endommager les forêts. Ces deux résultats sont possibles mais peu probables car nous nous adapterons aux machines qui seront à notre disposition et nous les contrôlerons.

La récolte mécanisée est une solution à l'insuffisance de main d'œuvre dans ce genre de travail. En dépit du coût élevé des machines, on constate une baisse de prix du bois livré aux usines. On prévoit de plus qu'après quelque temps personne ne songera plus à éclaircir les forêts avant la période "commerciale", ce qui veut dire que ceux qui s'occupent de sylviculture pourront agir sur la forêt pour contrôler, sans aucun frais, et parfois d'une manière lucrative, l'espèce, la densité et la qualité.

EXPOSÉ 12

La Technique D'éclaircie – Moyen et Problème d'une Silviculture Soignée

Par S. HÄBERLE

La technique d'éclaircie doit s'orienter à trois objectifs principaux:
- en premier lieu elle doit satisfaire le but à long terme qui est d'obtenir des peuplements à plein degré de couvert et constitués par des arbres de grande dimension et de belle forme.
- ensuite, comme but à terme moyen, il s'agit de créer dans le peuplement un systeme de voies pour faciliter toutes les opérations posterieures.
- enfin, comme but à court terme, elle doit garantir la rentabilité des travaux de récolte.

Pour l'épicéa (*Picea abies*) un procédé est recommandé qui comprendrait la période allant de l'âge de perchis jusqu'à la maturité du peuplement, et qui peut satisfaire à la fois les trois objectifs sus-cités.

En ce contexte il faut prendre en considération les règles suivantes:

Plus un peuplement est jeune, plus des coupes schématiques sont convenables.

En ce qui concerne la technique du travail, les coupes schématiques s'effectuent à l'aide d'un "harvester pour faibles dimensions" qui peut établir des lignes de 4 à 5 mètres de largeur en réalisant les travaux suivants: abattage, ébranchage, façonnage, ramassage et déposition du bois dans les lignes.

La larguer des bandes restantes varie de 20 à 30 mètres. Sur ces bandes l'intervention s'effectue en forme d'une éclaircie sélective.

Dans des peuplements jeunes les tiges sont façonnées en troncs d'une longueur standard de 2 mètres, tandis que les arbres provenant des peuplements d'un âge plus avancé se façonnent comme bois long.

Dans des futaie le systéme SERIAS doit s'appliquer. Il s'agit là d'élaguer et de cortiquer les arbres à récolter sur pied, une intervention sélective, qui se realise sans aucun dommage chez le peuplement restant.

S'il n'y a pas de revenu à cause d'une relation défavorable entre le prix du bois et le coût du façonnage, on peut favoriser les arbres d'avenir en tuant leurs concurrents au moyen des substances toxiques, appliquées en forme d'une cartouche d'injection selon un procédé du docteur STERZIK.

Cette mesure ne peut pas être pratiquée oû l'attaque et l'expansion de coléoptères sont à craindre.

En ce cas il faut recourir aux méthodes mécaniques même si celles-ci soient déficitaires à court terme, car l'objectif à long terme, c'est la forêt soignée, capable de remplir ses fonctions écologiques et économiques de façon adéquate. Ce but doit prévaloir indépendamment de la relation prix-coût au moment des travaux d'éclaircie.

EXPOSÉ 13

Éclaircissage Forestier: État des Choses dans le Nord-Ouest Pacifique

Par D. E. AULERICH

L'éclaircissage des forêts de pin Douglas (*Pseudotsuga menziesii*) de la région du Nord-Ouest Pacifique devient de plus en plus fréquent au fur et à mesure que de nombreux jeunes plants remplacent les vieux. Bien que la majeure partie des opérations en cours soient effectuées par des véhicules à traction horizontale, des tracteurs munis de chenilles ou de pneumatiques, on se tourne de plus en plus vers la technique de l'éclaircissage à câble. Cet état de choses est dû principalement à la configuration escarpée du terrain et à la fragilité des sols qui caractérisent une grande partie de la région.

Le responsable des coupes doit résoudre deux problèmes majeurs: mettre les forestiers à même de traiter des jeunes bois ainsi que se procurer du matériel adéquat.

Les problèmes de charriage méchanique des jeunes bois sont à l'étude. Les résultats permettront d'élaborer de futurs outillages et de futurs techniques destinées à traiter et, en premier lieu, à hisser les jeunes bois le long de pentes abruptes.

EXPOSÉ 14

PROBLÉMES DE L'EXTRACTION DES ÉCLAIRCIES AU MOYEN DE TREUILS À CÂBLES DANS LE ROYAUMME-UNI

Par J. A. DRUMMOND

Les grues à câbles, utilisées au Royaume-Uni, sont des marques d'une amplitude courte ou moyenne. Elles sont sensibles au rendement d'éclaircies, particulièrement dans les périodes initialles.

Les dégâts dans la récolte et au sol sont très limités et il n'y a aucune indication d'instabilité aux vents produits par les esquisses utilisées.

EXPOSÉ 15

SYSTÈMES MÉCANISÉS D'ÉCLAIRCISSAGE

Par CARL J. BREDBERG

L'augmentation rapide des coûts d'éclaircir a provoqué une réduction du volume de ces travaux. Si l'on estime que l'éclaircie sera nécessaire dans le traitement futur des peuplements, nous serons obligés de développer des nouvelles machines et des méthodes spécialement conçues en vue d'obtenir une haute productivité et les frais basses, dans le domaine de l'exploitation de bois de petites dimensions. Le principe de manipuler les petites arbres en paquets, offre une solution avantageuse. Un obstacle sérieux à la mécanisation sont cependant les dégâts au peuplement, qui sont causés surtout par des véhicules tous-terrains de transport. Un développement coûteux qui fait perdre du temps est nécessaire pour résoudre ce problème. L'alternative est que dans l'avenir nous serons obligés de renoncer à nos possibilités d'éclaircir.

ZUSAMMENFASSUNG DER STUDIEN

REFERAT 1

VORLÄUFIGE ERGEBNISSE EINIGER NEUER DÄNISCHER DURCHFORSTUNGSVERSUCHE
MIT FICHTE

Von H. BRYNDUM

Dieser Bericht enthält vorläufige Ergebnisse zweier Fichtendurchforstungsversuche (*Picea abies*) auf fruchtbarem Boden in Dänemark. Die Versuche sind 1953 und 1960 in jungen noch nicht durchforsteten Pflanzungen angelegt worden; die letzte Aufnahme stammt aus dem Jahre 1973. Die Behandlungen, angepasst an Grundfläche, sind wie folgt:

A, B, C, D und D–B, entsprechen keiner, schwacher, mittelstarker, sehr starker und im jungen Bestand sehr starker, später schwacher Durchforstung.

In beiden Versuchen war der Massenzuwachs während der Versuchsperiode von 20 bzw 13 Jahren beinahe der gleiche bei allen Behandlungen, mit etwas Mehrzuwachs bei den stärkeren Graden in den ersten Jahren. Der Höhenwuchs wird nicht oder nur wenig von der Durchforstung beeinflusst, wogegen der Durchmesserzuwachs mit zunehmendem Durchforstungsgrad stark zunimmt. Die Durchforstungsstärke hat einen entscheidenden Einfluss auf die Dimensionsverteilung der Gesamterzeugung gehabt; mit steigender Intensität der Durchforstung verlagert sich die produzierte Holzmasse von den mittleren zu den höheren Durchmesserklassen.

Die Qualität des Holzes ist etwas verringert mit zunehmender Durchforstung, die Kronenansatzhöhe wird kürzer, die Abholzigkeit grösser ebenso wie der Astdurchmesser. Es wurde kein Zusammenhang zwischen Fäulnisbefall und Durchforstung nachgewiesen, es steigt aber die Sturmfallgefahr mit zunehmender Durchforstungsstärke, besonders bei grösseren Bestandeshöhen. Während der ersten Jahre nach den starken Eingriffen ergibt sich auch Schneebruchgefahr, später allerdings, wenn sich regelmässige Baumkronen geformt haben, ist ein stark durchforsteter Bestand schneebruchsicher.

Bisher haben die starken Durchforstungen den grössten Nettoerlös ergeben. Die Gesamtwertleistung, d.i. der Wert der Durchforstungen und des Bestandes, im Alter 38 bzw 34 Jahren ist bei der starker Durchforstung am grössten; das gleiche gilt für den Kapitalwert. Die Wertleistung steigt noch mit zunehmendem Alter erheblich an.

REFERAT 2

AUSWIRKUNGEN DER REIHENDURCHFORSTUNG AUF DEN ZUWACHS

Von G. J. HAMILTON

Die Ergebnisse von fünf Reihendurchforstungsversuchen legen die folgenden Schlüsse nahe:

a. ein Verlust an Gesamtderbholzleistung tritt im Zusammenhang mit dem neutralen Durchforstungssystem – unbedingt in der Reihendurchforstung – auf.

b. der Einflussbereich der Reihendurchforstung beschränkt sich zum grossen Teil auf die den abgeräumten Reihen nächstliegenden Reihen.

c. die positive Reaktion der Aussenreihen (d.h. der unmittelbaren Nachbarn der abgeräumten Reihen) steigt merklich an, wenn die Zahl der nebeneinanderliegenden Durchforstungsreihen vergrössert wird und.

d. grössere Verluste an Gesamtderbholzleistung entstehen in Verbindung mit vergrösserter Anzahl von nebeneinanderliegenden Durchforstungsreihen.

REFERAT 3

ENTWICKLUNG UND ERTRAG UNDURCHFORSTETER FICHTENPFLANZUNGEN IN WESTNORWEGEN

Von O. BØRSET

Es wurden 31 undurchforstete, dicht bepflanzte *Picea abies* Flächen in Westnorwegen untersucht, wobei die Oberhöhe bei den meisten Flächen 16–25 m betrug. Die Flächen lagen hauptsächlich an steilen Hängen in guter Lage und in feuchtem Klima (jährliche Niederschlagsmenge 1500–3000 mm). Die meisten Bestände wurden mit einem Pflanzabstand von weniger als 1,5 m begründet.

Die totale Massenproduktion unterschied sich weniger von derjenigen in durchforsteten Beständen. Der Verlust an Masse in der Selbstdurchforstung betrug fast immer weniger als 10%. Tote Bäume scheinen früh unterdrückt worden zu sein und sind im allgemeinen abgestorben bevor sie die Sägeholzgrösse erreicht haben. Bei einer mittleren

Höhe von 15 m bestand im allgemeinen mehr als 80 % des Volumens aus Bäumen mit einem BHD von über 11 cm. Bei einer mittleren Höhe von 20 m machten die Bäume mit BHD über 17 cm mehr als 80% des Volumens aus. Gesundheit und Stabilität wurden als genügend betrachtet.

Die untersuchten undurchforsteten Bestände haben sich besser entwickelt als auf Grund von Erfahrungen aus Durchforstungsversuchen in anderen Teilen nördlicher Gebiete zu erwarten war. Der Grund mag im vorteilhaften Wasserhaushalt der Bestände (hohe Niederschläge) zu suchen sein.

REFERAT 4

DIE ENTWICKLUNG VON DURCHFORSTUNGS- UND ERNTE-VERFAHREN IN JUNGEN FICHTEN- UND KIEFERNSTÄNDEN

Von G. J. GALLAGHER

Versuchsergebnisse haben gezeigt, dass der Ausheib von ein Drittel des stehenden Vorrats gleich bei der ersten Durchforstung von Sitka-Fichte (*Picea sitchensis*) keinen grossen Verlust von Massenzuwachs verursacht und bei der Drehkiefer sich noch etwas weniger bemerkbar macht. Eine grosse Anzahl verschiedener Durchforstungsverfahren mässigen Grades scheint die Massenleistung nur wenig zu beeinflussen; Plenterdurchforstungen dürften vielleicht ein wenig besser sein. Diese Ergebnisse haben zu einer Untersuchung der Reihendurchforstung mit Entnahme jeder dritten oder zweiten Reihe geführt. Von den untersuchten Verfahren sind diese Reihendurchforstungen mit dem geringsten Kostenaufwand verbunden. Diese Durchforstungsverfahren wurden in Verbindung mit verschiedenen Holzernte- und Bringungsverfahren geprüft. Das Ausbringen ganzer Bäume mit Grossmaschinen hat sich noch nicht so erfolgreich erwiesen wie einfachere Verfahren. Die Hochseilsysteme werden für hügeliges Terrain entwickelt. *Pinus contorta* scheint gegen Sturmschaden mehr empfindlich zu sein als die Sitka-Fichte. Stürme der jüngsten Zeit haben an der Sitka-Fichte viel weniger Schaden verursacht als erwartet.

REFERAT 5

NEUSEELÄNDER ERFAHRUNGEN MIT PINUS RADIATA

Von W. R. J. SUTTON

Undurchforstete *Pinus radiata* Bestände mit langen Umtriebszeiten haben ein hohes Risiko von Krankheiten und Schädlinge befallen zu werden. Die ersten umfangreicheren Versuche Durchforstungen mit einem Reinerlös durchzuführen brachten keinen höheren Gesamtzuwachs und keine höhere Durchforstungserträge. Daraufhin wurde ein neues Bewirtschaftungssystem entwickelt, dass in der Gesamtzuwachsleistung gleichwertig und wirtschaftlich und waldbaulich überlegen war. Dieses System arbeitet mit weiten Anfangsverbänden, starker früher Durchforstung ohne Verwertung des Holzes und starker Wertästung.

REFERAT 6

FORSCHUNG IN DER DURCHFORSTUNG IN SÜDAFRIKA

Von A. VAN LAAR

In Südafrika sind Pflanzerbandversuche (Correlated Curve Trend Experiments) angelegt worden zur Erforschung des Zusammenhanges zwischen Bestandesdichte und Wachstumsablauf gleichjähriger Waldbestände. Die einzelne Wuchsreihe umfasst 8 Verbandsflächen mit Stammzahlen zwischen 125 und 3000 je Hektar. Der Versuch wird kombiniert mit einer Erfassung der Volumenleistung auf Durchforstungsflächen, die ein Teil des Versuchsplans sind. Dies ermöglicht die Anwendung von C.C.T.-Wuchsreihen für die Wachstumsprognose in Durchforstung-flächen. Die Gesamtwuchsleistung sowie auch andere ertragskundliche Grössen werden entscheidend durch Bestandesdichte beeinflusst.

Zusätzlich sind Durchforstungsversuche in *Pinus radiata* und *Populus deltoides*-Beständen angelegt worden, entweder als vollständig randomisierte Versuchsanlage oder als Block-oder als Spaltanlage, im letzteren Fall in Kombination mit Ästungsbehandlungen. Wegen der Existenz von Wechselwirkungen ist die gleichzeitige Erforschung der Einflüsse von Durchforstung und Ästung auf den Wachstumsablauf von Kiefernbeständen in Zweifaktorversuchen empfehlenswert.

Durchforstungsversuche in *Populus deltoides*- Beständen zeigten die Überlegenheit der mittleren Grundflächenhaltung als Kriterium für Bestandesdichte. Die Versuche mit *Pinus radiata* und *Populus deltoides* zeigten einen kurvilinearen Zusammenhang zwischen Bestandesdichte und Volumenleistung.

Zur Erfassung des Konkurrenzdruckes innerhalb der in unterschiedlicher Stärke durchforsteten Flächen wurden Konkurrenzvariablen definiert und zunächst mit dem Zuwachs von Einzelbäumen korreliert. Der Zusammenhang zwischen diesen Konkurrenzvariablen und dem Zuwachs wurde kovarianzanalytisch untersucht.

REFERAT 7

Messungen des Wachsraums – eine Ergänzung von Durchforstungsversuchen

Von A. M. JENSEN

In einem 76 jährigen Bestand von Fichten (*Picea abies*) nahe einem Durchforstungsversuche sind an 247 Einzelbäumen genaue Massenzuwachsmessungen gemacht. Standraum ist gemessen und berechnet unter Berücksichtigung In einem 76 jährigen Bestand von Fichten (*Picea abies*) nahe einem Durchforstungsversuche sind auf 247 Einzelbämen genaue Massenzuwachsmenssungen gemacht. Standraum is gemessen und berechnet unter Berücksichtigung verschiedener Konkurrenzverhältnisse. Die Ergebnisse der Einzelbaummessungen sind mit dem Ergebnis des Durchforstungsversuchs vergleichen. Die Verwendung von Standraummessungen ist schliesslich diskutiert.

REFERAT 8

Der Einfluss verschiedener Durchforstungsarten auf Wachstum und Bestandsschäden. Untersuchungsergebnisse aus Fichtenbeständen in der Bundesrepublik Deutschland

Von H. KRAMER

Das materielle Ziel der Fichtenwirtschaft (*Picea abies*) in Mitteleuropa, der höchste Waldreinertrag, beinhaltet eine optimale Zuwachs- und Wertleistung und die Vermeidung von Bestandesschäden. Weite Bestandesbegründung und frühzeitige Stammzahlverminderung erhöhen den Wertzuwachs und die Bestandessicherheit gegen Schnee und Wind. Zur Rationalisierung der ersten Durchforstungen eng begründeter Fichtenbestände werden Auslese-, Reihen- oder Gassendurchforstungen sowie Kombinationen dieser Durchforstungsarten empfohlen. Die Auswirkungen der schematischen Eingriffe auf Zuwachs und Bestandesschäden werden untersucht. Ein Vergleich von Niederdurchforstung, Auslesedurchforstung und Reihendurchforstung (Tabelle 8.1) zeigt, dass die Niederdurchforstung betriebswirtschaftlich extrem schlecht abschneidet. Auslese-und Reihendurchforstung sind etwa gleich günstig. Gemäss der Zuwachsanalyse (Tabelle 8.2) haben Niederdurchforstung und Auslesedurchforstung nahezu den gleichen Volumenzuwachs. Der 5-jährige Massenzuwachs ist 8% niedriger, wirkt sich aber auf die Umtriebszeit von 100 Jahren (mit 0,6%) kaum aus. Der Zuwachs der 400 stärksten Bäume (=Zukunftsbäume) ist bei der Reihendurchforstung 5%, bei der Auslesedurchforstung 14% höher als bei der Niederdurchforstung. Die frühe starke Durchforstung hat die Kronenentwicklung gefördert (Tabelle 8.3), am besten bei der Auslesedurchforstung.

Bei einer extremen Reihendurchforstung (Entnahme jeder 4. Reihe eines in 3 m-Reihenabstand stehenden Fichtenbestandes) mit Durchforstungsgassen von 6 m Breite in Brilon konnte gegenüber der individuellen Niederdurchforstung kein gesicherter Zuwachsverlust (im Mittel 3%) nachgewiesen werden (Tabelle 8.4).

Ein heute 100-jähriger Fichtenbestand im Harz, bei dem vor 45 Jahren 2/3 des Vorrates durch Entnahme jeder 2. und 3. Reihe entnommen wurde, zeigt eine sehr hohe Massen- und Wertleistung (s. Tabelle 8.5).

Für die Maschinelle Stammzahlverminderung extrem dichter, 8 m hoher Fichtenbestände wurde eine Spezialraupe verwendet, die im Abstand von 8 m 2,5 m breite Gassen abschnitt und niederdrückte. Die Massnahme war extrem billig. Folgeschäden sind nicht eingetreten.

Bei Erstdurchforstung unter Verwendung einer Kurzholzmethode (2 m langes Industrieholz mit Rinde) wurden drei verschiedene Gassendurchforstungen geprüft (Gassenbreite 4,50 m Gassenabstand von Gassenrand zu Gassenrand 3 m bis 15 m). Mit Ausnahme des extrem engen Gassenabstandes wurde der schematische Eingriff mit einer Auslesedurchforstung im Zwischenstreifen kombiniert. Die reine Gassendurchforstung im engen Abstand hatte die grösste Leistung, jedoch auch die stärksten Schäden an den Bäumen. Boden- und Wurzelschäden wurden durch die auf den Gassen liegende Reisigdecke vermieden.

Bei Verwendung der Baumholzerntemethode werden i.a. grössere Schäden (besonders am Stammfuss) als bei der Kurzholzmethode verursacht.

Windschäden treten besonders bei älteren Fichtenbeständen auf. Stärkere Durchforstungseingriffe in Jungbeständen auch Reihen- und Gassendurchforstungen – haben die Sturmkatastrophe vom November 1972 i.a. gut überstanden. Durch Schneebruch sind dagegen besonders die jüngeren Fichtenbestände gefährdet. Das Ausfallprozent durch Schnee steigt proportional mit dem Höhen /Durchmesser= Verhältnis und umgekehrt mit dem Kronenprozent (s. Abbildung 8.1 und 8.2). Innerhalb eines Bestandes nimmt der Schneebruch mit zunehmendem Durchmesser deutlich ab (Abbildung 8.3). Die Erfahrungen über Schneebruchschäden nach Gassen- und Reihendurchforstung sind uneinheitlich, abhängig vom Bestandeszustand und dem Zeitabstand zwischen Durchforstung und Eintritt des

Schadens. Unmittelbar nach der Durchforstung ist der Bestand am labilsten. Der nach schematischer Durchforstung auftretende Schaden ist unbedeutend, da hierbei lediglich die schwachen Bäume betroffen werden, die bei einer Niederdurchforstung bereits entnommen wären (s. Abbildung 8.4).

REFERAT 9

GESICHTSPUNKTE ZUR WAHL VON WALDBAUMETHODE UND ERNTETECHNIK BEI DURCHFORSTUNGEN

Von JÖRAN FRIES

Schäden durch schwere Maschinen in Durchforstungen sind untersucht worden. Der Umfang der Schäden am Boden und an Wurzeln steigt schnell mit abnehmender Tragfähigkeit der Böden. Reisig und Zweige von gefällten Bäumen auf den Transportwegen reduziert die Schäden stark. Schäden an Fichtenwurzeln stärker als 2 cm verursachen Fäule, die, wenn der Schaden nahe am Baum gelegen ist (<0.5 m), in den meisten Fällen auch zur Stammfäule führen. Schäden an Kiefer verursachen nur sehr selten Fäuleangriffe. Ein Beispiel ist gegeben, wie man mit Simulierung die beste Kombination von Waldbaumethode und Erntetechnik finden kann.

REFERAT 10

DER EINFLUSS VERSCHIEDENER DURCHFORSTUNGSSYSTEME AUF SCHÄDEN AN BODEN UND BÄUMEN

Von H. A. FROEHLICH

Mit zunehmender Mechanisierung wächst die Sorge, dass Durchforstung potentiell dem Boden und den Bäumen schaden kann. Der tatsächliche Wachstumsverlust der Baumrückstände oder Sämlinge nach dem endgültigen Fällen ist noch nicht genau bestimmt worden. Durchforstungsstudien zeigten sehr unterschiedliche Ergebnisse. Diese Ergebnisse sind so verschieden infolge von Unterschieden in Standort-, Bestand- und Betriebsfaktoren. Es wird ein allgemeiner Begriff der Wechselbeziehungen dieser Faktoren gegeben. Bodenstruktur und Bodenfeuchtigkeit zur Zeit der Durchforstung haben die grösste Auswirkung auf Bodendichtigkeit. Der Einfluss von Müll und Baumzertrümmerung auf Passierbarkeit des Bodens sind ebenfalls als Faktoren genannt worden, die Unterschiede in Boden- und Baumschäden hervorrufen. Baumarten unterscheiden sich erheblich in ihrer Empfänglichkeit für Schäden durch Bodendichtigkeit, abgebrochene Wurzeln oder Stammwunden.

Boden- und Baumschäden infolge verschiedener Durchforstungssysteme können nicht völlig von den Standort- und Beststandfaktoren getrennt werden. Der Hauptunterschied in der Auswirkung verschiedener Durchforstungssysteme ist offenbar eine Folge des Bodendrucks und der Intensität oder Häufigkeit ihrer Anwendung. Eine Untersuchung der Durchforstung eines 35-Jahre alten Douglastannenbestandes mit Hochseilsystem und Raupenschlepper zeigt einen grossen Unterschied im Ausmass der Bodenbeschädung und Bodendichtigkeit. Relativ geringer Unterschied wurde im prozentualen Anteil der Stämme mit Wunden beobachtet. Baumwunden durch Traktordurchforstung waren im allgemeinen nahe dem Boden und möglicherweise anfälliger für Wurzelinfektionen als Hochseilwunden.

Viel Forschung ist notwendig, um eine Vorherbestimmung des tatsächlichen Wachstumsverlusts durch sichtbaren Boden- und Stammschäden zu ermöglichen.

REFERAT 11

DIE MASCHINEN KOMMEN, DIE MASCHINEN KOMMEN

Von HAROLD E. YOUNG

Die erfolgreiche Anwendung der motorisierten Holzhächselmaschine von Morbark Industries, Inc. als wesentlicher Teil eines mechanisierten Holzernteverfahrens und die ebenfalls erfolgreiche industrielle Verwendung der Holzhächsel mit Rinde durch Industrie-zweige, die daraus neue Holzprodukte herstellen, hat eine völlige neue Ära im Ernteverfahren wie auch in der Verwendung der Holzhauptproduktion eingeleitet. Der einträgliche Absatzmarkt hat eine Anzahl von Maschinenfabriken ermutigt, Maschinen verschiedener Grössen mit Fremd- und Eigenantrieb zu konstruieren, die sowohl beim Kahlschlag als auch im Ausleseverfahren Verwendung finden können.

Viele Forstwirtschaftler sind jetzt besorgt, dass die Anwendung solcher Maschinen zu einem Übereinschlag und zu Waldschäden führen wird. Beides ist möglich, doch unwahrscheinlich, da wir uns in zunehmendem Masse an die uns zur Verfügung stehenden Maschinen gewöhnen und sie zu kontrollieren lernen.

Mechanisierte Holzernte ist die Antwort auf den bestehenden Forstarbeitermangel. Trotz der hohen Anschaffungskosten der Maschinen ist aber dennoch ein Absinken des Holzpreises beim Abliefern bei den Sägewerken zu verzeichnen.

Es wird ferner erwartet, dass es in Zukunft keinen "vorkommerziellen" Einschlag mehr geben wird, was bedeuten würde, dass professionelle Forstwirtschaftler den Wald manipulieren können, um die Arten, Dichte und Qualität zu kontrollieren, und zwar kostenlos und manchmal sogar mit Gewinn.

REFERAT 12

DIE DURCHFORSTUNGSTECHNIK ALS MITTEL UND PROBLEM EINER PFLEGLICHEN
WALDBEWIRTSCHAFTUNG

Von S. HÄBERLE

Die Durchforstungstechnik muss sich an drei Zielsphären orientieren:
     einer langfristigen, welche anstrebt, im Umtriebsalter vollbestockte Flächen möglichst wertvoller und stark dimensionierter Bäume zu haben,
     einer mittelfristigen, welche der Bestandeserschliessung gewidmet ist
     und einer kurzfristigen, welche die Wirtschaftlichkeit der momentanen Holzerntemassnahmen im Auge hat.
Es wird versucht, für die ganze Spanne der Fichtendurchforstung vom jungen Stangenholz bis zum Baumholz Arbeitstechniken darzustellen, welche diesen drei Zielsphären in optimaler Kombination gerecht werden.
     Dabei gelten folgende Grundsätze:
     Je jünger der Bestand ist, desto eher sind schematische Eingriffe zulässig. Arbeitstechnisch werden die schematischen Eingriffe mit Hilfe eines Durchforstungs-Vollernters bewerkstelligt, der Gassen von 4–5 m Breite herstellen kann und folgende Bearbeitungsgänge ausführt: Fällen, Entasten, Einschneiden, Sammeln, Ablegen in der Gasse.
     Die Gassen haben Abstände von 20–30 m. Auf den dazwischen verbleibenden Streifen finden selektive Entnahmen statt. In jüngeren Beständen werden 2 m – Standardlängen ausgeformt, in mittelalten und älteren Beständen eher Langsortimente.
     In Baumhölzern kommt das SERIAS – System zur Anwendung, bei dem die zu erntenden Bäume stehend entastet und entrindet werden. Das System gestattet sehr bestandesschonende selektive Durchforstungseingriffe.
     Ist der ausscheidende Bestand zufolge ungüstiger Relationen zwischen Holzpreisen und Aufarbeitungskosten nicht mit Gewinn verkäuflich, so kann man die Zukunftsstämme in der Weise begünstigen, dass man ihre Bedränger mit Hilfe der von Dr STERZIK entwickelten Pflegepatrone abtötet. Dieses Vorgehen ist nur zulässig, wenn keine Käfergefahr besteht; andernfalls lassen sich mechanische Eingriffe nicht umgehen, auch wenn die Massnahme kurzfristig gesehen defizitär ist, denn das langfristige Ziel eines gepflegten Waldes verlangt Durchforstungen ganz unabhängig von der momentanen Preis-Kosten-Situation.

REFERAT 13

DURCHFORSTUNG: DER STATUS IM PAZIFISCHEM NORDWESTEN DER USA

Von D. E. AULERICH

Mehr und mehr werden Durchforstungen von Douglasienbeständen (*Pseudotsuga menziesii*) im pazifischem Nordwesten der USA durchgeführt, wo Jungbestände den Platz des Urwaldes in zunehmendem Masse einnehmen. Obwohl Ketten- und gummibereifte Fahrzeuge zur Rückung bevorzugt herangezogen werden, wächst das Interesse für Durchforstungsseilbahnen hauptsächlich der steilen Hänge und des leicht erodierten Bodens wegen.
     Schwierigkeiten bei der Aufbringung und Rückung von Durchforstungshölzern ergeben sich besonders bei der Umstellung, die für die Arbeitskräfte notwendig wird, und bei der Anschaffung von Maschinen.
     Die Probleme, die sich mit Rückeanlagen- und systemen bei der Aufbringung von Schwachholz ergeben, werden hier aufgezeigt. Diese Information wird für die zukünftige Entwicklung von Rückeanlagen und- methoden hauptsächlich für Schwachholz auf steilem, schwer zugänglichem Gelände wertvoll sein.

REFERAT 14

PROBLEME DER AUSBRINGUNG VON DURCHFORSTUNGSHOLZ MITTELS SEILKRAN
IM VEREINIGTEN KÖNIGREICH (GROSSBRITANNIEN)

Von J. DRUMMOND

Seilkräne, die in Grossbritannien benutzt werden, sind Kurz- und Mittelbereichtypen. Drahtseilkräne sind für Durchforstungsprodukte und Erstdurchforstungen anwendbar.

Schäden von Bestand und Boden sind sehr beschränkt. Bei der von uns ausgelegten Anlage besteht nur geringe Windempfindlichkeit.

REFERAT 15

MECHANISIERTE DURCHFORSTUNGSVERFAHREN

Von C. J. BREDBERG

Die schnell steigenden Durchforstungskosten haben zu einer Abnahme der Durchforstungseingriffe geführt. Wenn wir der Ansicht sind, dass die Durchforstung in der zukünftigen Bestandsbehandlung notwendig wird, müssen wir neue Maschinen und Systeme entwickeln, die für hohe Produktivität und niedrige Kosten in Bezug auf kleine Bäume konstruiert sind. Das Prinzip, Bündel von kleinen Bäumen zu hantieren, bietet günstige Lösungen. Ein ernstes Hinderniss der Mechanisierung sind aber die Bestandsschäden, die vor allem von geländegängigen Transportfahrzeugen verursacht werden. Eine teuere und zeitraubende Entwicklung ist notwendig, um dieses Problem lösen zu können. Die Alternative ist, dass wir in Zukunft auf unsere Durchforstungsmöglichkeiten verzichten müssen.

PRELIMINARY RESULTS FROM SOME NEW DANISH THINNING EXPERIMENTS WITH NORWAY SPRUCE ON FERTILE SOILS

By H. BRYNDUM

Danish Forest Experiment Station, Klampenborg, Denmark

Introduction

Before 1950 there were only four regular thinning experiments in conifers in Denmark, three in Norway spruce (*Picea abies*) and one in Sitka spruce (*P. sitchensis*). The results from all of these experiments have now been published (Bornebusch 1933 and 1937, Henriksen 1961, Bryndum 1964, 1969 and 1974), and only one of these experiments is still in existence.

In 1953 the Danish Forest Experiment Station again began establishing thinning experiments, especially in Norway spruce, and during the next 14 years experiments were started in young spruce stands in the most important forest localities in this country. The experiments are primarily based on selective thinnings of varying intensity, starting when the stand is fairly young, with the purpose of elucidating the influence of different densities on the development of the stand, its stability, and value yield.

This is a report, chiefly through tabular comparisons and figures, of the main features of a recent collection of data from the two earliest experiments in this series, the Clausholm and the East Lolland experiments.

Description of the Localities and the Experimental Layout

THE CLAUSHOLM EXPERIMENT was established in autumn 1953 in an 18 year old, unthinned Norway spruce plantation. It is situated in east Jutland; the height above sea level is about 50 m, the annual precipitation amounts to 595 mm, the annual mean temperature is 7·3°C. The ground is flat; the soil is comparatively deep and consists of clay-mixed fine sand with a low podsolization, the clay content at the depth of 70 cm is approximately 15%. The planting took place in the spring of 1938 with 2 year old plants, spaced at 1×1 m. The previous crop was also Norway spruce. The stand data at the time of establishment appear in Table 1.1*.

THE EAST LOLLAND EXPERIMENT was established in autumn 1960 in three stands of an average age of 21 years. It is situated in Lolland, one of the southern islands; the height above sea level is

---
* Preliminary results, after the first 12 years of the experiment, have previously been published (eg Bryndum 1967).

5 to 10 m, the annual precipitation amounts to 605 mm; the annual mean temperature is 8·0°C. The ground is flat, the soil is shallow with a high groundwater table and very clayey, the clay content at the depth of 75 cm being, on average, 27%. Planting was done in spring 1946, and in 1938, with 2/2 plants spaced at 1·25×1·25 m or 1·25×1·50 m. The site was previously occupied by old hardwood forest. The mean stand data at establishment of the experiment are stated in Table 1.2.

The experiments involve the following 5 *treatments*:

A thinning — no thinning
B thinning — light thinning
C thinning — medium-heavy thinning
D–B thinning — in youth very heavy, later very light thinning
D thinning — very heavy thinning

In principle, the thinning treatment is determined by the basal area. During the initial years the thinning intensity was the same in the D and D–B grades; from stand height 12 to 14 m the heavy thinnings in the D–B grade was to be discontinued.

In the Clausholm experiment only the A grade was replicated; in the East Lolland experiment all 5 treatments were replicated 4 times.

Results of Assessments

The experiments were measured each 4th (or 5th) year; the results of the latest measurement of the stands in autumn 1973 are represented in a condensed form in Tables 1.1 and 1.2. They further show the total thinning volume in the respective experimental periods and the mean volume increment from planting and during the observation period.

The intensity of the thinning grades practised should be apparent from Figures 1.1 and 1.2 which show the development of the stem numbers, and from Figures 1.3 and 1.4, which show the basal area development in the two experiments.

The relationship of thinning intensity to volume increment in the two experiments can be studied in greater detail in Tables 1.3 and 1.4, in which, for each thinning grade, mean basal area and annual volume increment are stated for shorter periods as well as for the whole of the experimental period. Further, the relative periodic increments are represented graphically in Figures 1.5 and 1.6.

TABLE 1.1
THE CLAUSHOLM THINNING EXPERIMENT

Grade of thinning	CROP					Thinning a. 1953–73	Increment	
	N per ha	H_L m	D_g cm	G m²/ha	V m³/ha	V m³/ha	I_V 2–38 m³/ha	I_V 18–38 m³/ha
All grades	BEFORE FIRST THINNING AT YEAR 1953, 18 years							
	7865	6·3	6·1	23·23	88·9			
	AFTER THINNING AT YEAR 1973, 38 YEARS							
A	2693	17·5	14·1	42·12	407·3	95·1	14·0	20·8
B	2002	17·6	15·5	37·94	363·9	115·3	13·3	20·0
C	918	19·0	20·5	30·23	301·6	206·0	14·1	21·1
D–B	925	20·0	21·7	34·28	357·9	187·4	15·1	22·4
D	429	20·5	25·8	22·46	232·5	295·9	14·7	21·6

TABLE 1.2
THE EAST LOLLAND THINNING EXPERIMENT
(Each treatment is represented by 4 plots).

Grade of thinning	CROP					Thinning a. 1960–73	Increment	
	N per ha	H_L m	D_g cm	G m²/ha	V m³/ha	V m³/ha	I_V 4–34 m³/ha	I_V 21–34 m³/ha
All grades	BEFORE FIRST THINNING, at year 1960, 21 years							
	4962	8·0	8·5	27·03	124·8			
	AFTER THINNING, AT YEAR 1973, 34 YEARS							
A	3179	15·8	13·9	48·42	410·2	33·9	14·9	25·0
B	2396	16·8	15·3	43·97	389·9	73·5	15·6	25·6
C	1149	17·4	18·9	32·11	286·6	168·5	15·4	25·6
D–B	851	17·7	21·3	30·17	268·0	179·2	15·1	25·1
D	687	17·7	20·9	23·46	208·3	224·0	14·6	23·9

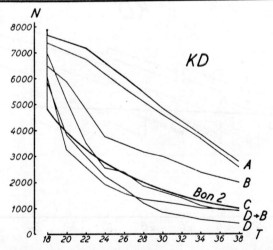

Figure 1.1 The Clausholm Experiment. Stem number development per hectare on each of the plots during the observation period, T, in years. The stem number curve for C. M. Møller's Site Class 2 (Møller 1933) is plotted for comparison, labelled Bon 2. KD is the designation of the Clausholm experiment.

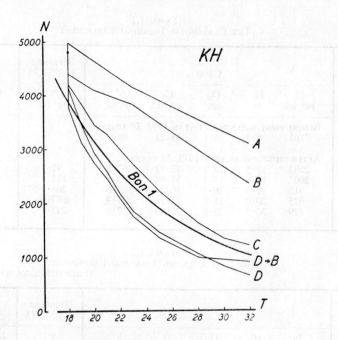

Figure 1.2   The East Lolland Experiment. Stem number development per hectare for each of the five thinning treatments during the observation period, T, in years, in one of the four blocks. The stem number curve for Site Class 1 is plotted for comparison, labelled Bon 1. KH is the designation of the East Lolland experiment.

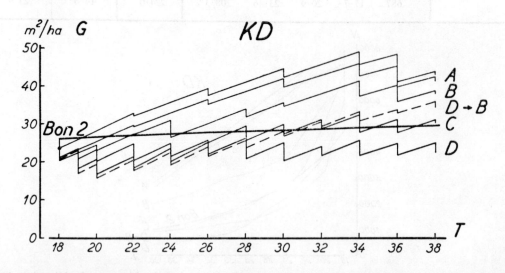

Figure 1.3   The Clausholm Experiment. Basal area development on each plot during the observation period, T, in years. The basal area between thinnings for C. M. Møller's Site Class 2 has been entered for comparison, labelled Bon 2.

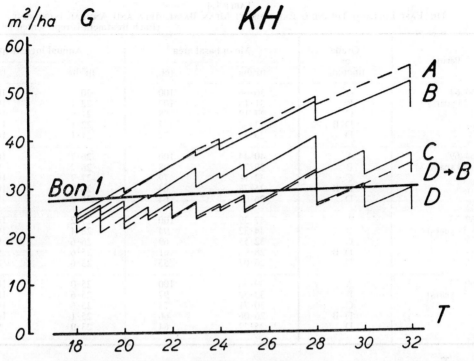

Figure 1.4 The East Lolland Experiment. Basal area development during the observation period, T, in years, in the five thinning grades of one of the blocks. Basal area between thinnings for Site Class 1 has been entered for comparison, labelled Bon 1.

TABLE 1.3
THE CLAUSHOLM THINNING EXPERIMENT: MEAN BASAL AREA AND ANNUAL INCREMENT

Period	Gade of thinning	Mean basal area		Annual increment	
		m²/ha	rel.	m³/ha	rel.
a. 1953–61 (18–26 years)	A	30·56	100	16·8	100
	B	26·30	86	16·4	98
	C	22·79	75	17·9	107
	D–B	20·05	66	19·2	114
	D	20·84	68	19·2	114
a. 1961–69 (26–34 years)	A	42·11	100	24·9	100
	B	35·54	84	23·7	95
	C	28·83	68	23·7	95
	D–B	27·42	65	25·3	102
	D	23·34	55	23·6	95
a. 1969–73 (34–38 years)	A	43·73	100	20·7	100
	B	38·08	87	19·6	95
	C	29·51	68	22·3	108
	D–B	33·41	76	23·0	111
	D	23·43	54	22·2	107
a. 1953–73 (18–38 years)	A	37·81	100	20·8	100
	B	32·35	86	20·0	96
	C	26·55	70	21·1	101
	D–B	25·67	68	22·4	108
	D	22·36	59	21·6	104

TABLE 1.4

THE EAST LOLLAND THINNING EXPERIMENT: MEAN BASAL AREA AND ANNUAL INCREMENT

(Each treatment is represented by 4 plots).

Period	Grade of thinning	Mean basal area		Annual increment	
		m²/ha	rel.	m³/ha	rel.
a. 1960–64	A	30·66	100	20·7	100
(21–25 years)	B	31·15	102	22·1	107
	C	27·12	88	21·9	106
	D–B	23·52	77	22·1	107
	D	23·54	77	21·1	102
a. 1964–69	A	40·44	100	26·7	100
(25–30 years)	B	39·77	98	26·2	98
	C	32·11	79	27·7	104
	D–B	25·78	64	26·9	101
	D	26·08	64	26·3	99
a. 1969–73	A	47·39	100	27·2	100
(30–34 years)	B	44·32	94	28·4	104
	C	32·55	69	26·6	98
	D–B	28·96	61	25·6	94
	D	26·07	55	23·6	87
a. 1960–73	A	39·56	100	25·0	100
(21–34 years)	B	38·52	97	25·6	102
	C	30·71	78	25·6	102
	D–B	26·06	66	25·1	100
	D	25·29	64	23·9	96

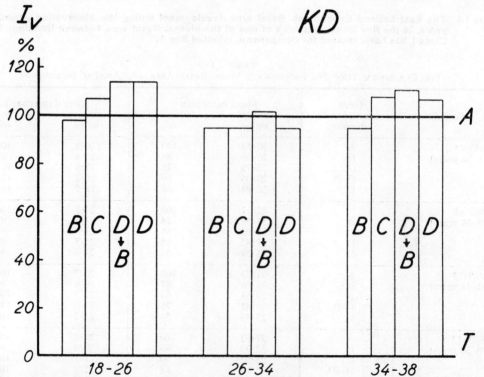

Figure 1.5   The Clausholm Experiment. Annual volume increment in the three age periods 18-26, 26-34, and 34-38 years expressed in percentages of the A-grade increment. T represents time in years.

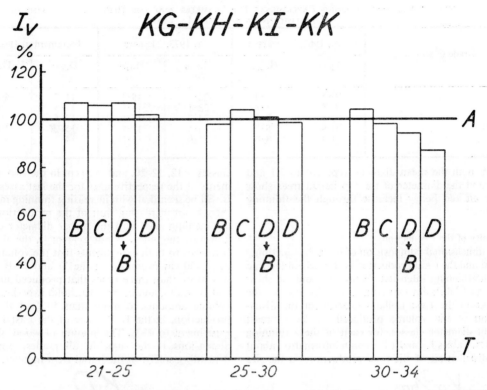

Figure 1.6   The East Lolland Experiment. Annual volume increment in the three age periods 21-25, 25-30 and 30-34 years, on average, expressed in percentage of the A-grade increment. T represents time in years. The symbols KG, KH, KI, KK are the designations of the four blocks of this experiment.

After 8 to 9 years, the relative mean basal areas in both experiments were reduced to about 55 in the D grade and about 70 in the C grade; in the B grade the aim was about 85. The response to stem-number reductions has not been the same in the two experiments. In the Clausholm experiment a considerable growth stimulation was recorded during the first 8 year as a result of heavy thinnings, whereas the growth stimulation was very modest during the first 9 years of the East Lolland experiment, and in

this experiment most marked in the medium-heavy C thinning. In the latter experiment the low mean basal area seems accordingly to involve a loss in volume production, a result which after 20 years has still not been clearly demonstrable at Clausholm.

Whereas the mean height, as could be seen from Tables 1.1 and 1.2, is increasing with increasing thinning intensity, this does not, or does at least only to a very modest extent, apply to the top height, as appears from Tables 1.5 and 1.6. On the other

TABLE 1.5
THE CLAUSHOLM THINNING EXPERIMENT: TOP DIAMETER AND TOP HEIGHT AT THE TIME OF ESTABLISHMENT AND AFTER 20 YEARS

Grade of thinning	A. 1953, 18 years		A. 1973, 38 years		Increment a. 1953–73	
	D_{dom} cm	H_{dom} m	D_{dom} cm	H_{dom} m	D_{dom} cm	H_{dom} m
A	11·7	8·2	23·2	20·7	11·5	12·5
B	11·6	8·2	24·1	20·5	12·5	12·3
C	11·6	7·8	26·0	20·8	14·4	13·0
D–B	11·4	7·7	27·4	21·6	16·0	13·9
D	11·1	8·0	29·3	21·3	18·2	13·3

TABLE 1.6
THE EAST LOLLAND THINNING EXPERIMENT: TOP DIAMETER AND TOP HEIGHT AT THE TIME OF
ESTABLISHMENT AND AFTER 13 YEARS

Grade of thinning	A. 1960, 21 years		A. 1973, 34 years		Increment a. 1960–73	
	D_{dom} cm	H_{dom} m	D_{dom} cm	H_{dom} m	D_{dom} cm	H_{dom} m
A	10·5	8·4	22·3	19·1	11·7	10·7
B	10·8	8·8	22·1	18·7	11·3	9·9
C	10·8	8·7	24·2	18·6	13·5	9·9
D–B	10·9	8·7	26·1	18·8	15·2	10·1
D	10·4	8·6	25·0	18·8	14·6	10·2

hand, both the mean diameter (cp. Tables 1.1 and 1.2) and the diameter of the top height trees show an even and heavy increase through the thinning grades.

Quality of the Production

The dimensional composition of both the remaining stand and the total production is strongly influenced by the thinning intensity. Figures 1.7 and 1.8 show for the Clausholm experiment and for one of the blocks in the East Lolland experiment the distribution of the volume produced by 5 cm breast height diameter classes, for each of the 5 thinning grades. Tables 1.7 and 1.8 contain information about the distribution of the total production on the size classes <12, 12–20, and >20 cm in the two experiments at the respective ages for the last assessment. It will be seen that with increasing thinning intensity there is an increasing shift of the production from the medium class into the higher diameter classes; however, this effect is not evident in the B grade. It applies to both experiments that the volume with $d_{1·3}$ >20 cm produced in the D and D–B grades was more than three times that produced in the A and B grades, and in the Clausholm experiment this volume amounts to more than 50% of the total production, in the D–B grade of the East Lolland experiment to 45%. The amount of wood of small dimensions is the same at all grades, obviously depending solely on the initial stem number.

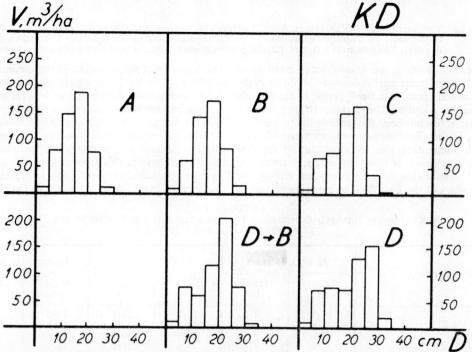

Figure 1.7   The Clausholm Experiment. Distribution of the total yield by breast height diameter classes in each of the treatments, assessed at age 38 years.

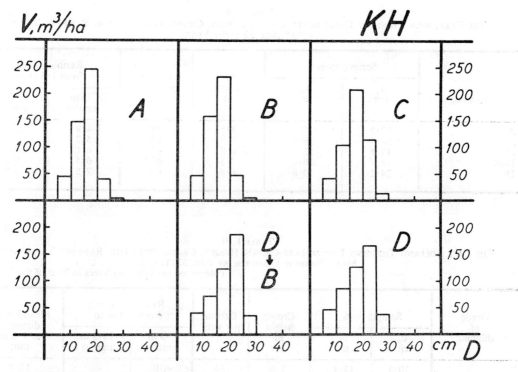

Figure 1.8 The East Lolland Experiment. Distribution of total yield by breast height diameter classes of the five treatments in one of the four blocks assessed at age 32 years.

Some other quality-deciding factors are represented in Tables 1.9 and 1.10; they are crown height, running taper, and, in the East Lolland experiment, mean branch thickness at the different grades. In addition, the crown percentage is stated. In the Clausholm experiment the measurements were taken on crop trees, in the East Lolland experiment on the thinnings. With increasing thinning intensity we find a falling crown height, increasing taper (from the B grade to the D grade of the order of 2 mm per running m) and at heights more than 2·5 m above ground level, increasing branch diameter (in the D–B and D grades approximately 20 mm at the height of 7·5 m). Crown length and crown percentage increase steeply with increasing thinning intensity.

TABLE 1.7
THE CLAUSHOLM THINNING EXPERIMENT: DISTRIBUTION OF THE TOTAL VOLUME PRODUCTION ON DIMENSION CLASSES AT AGE 38 YEARS

Grade of thinning	Breast-height diameter class					
	<12 cm		12–20 cm		>20 cm	
	m³/ha	%	m³/ha	%	m³/ha	%
A	137	27	282	56	84	17
B	110	23	273	57	96	20
C	107	21	198	39	204	40
D–B	111	20	148	27	286	51
D	111	21	116	22	301	57

TABLE 1.8
THE EAST LOLLAND THINNING EXPERIMENT: DISTRIBUTION OF THE TOTAL VOLUME PRODUCTION ON DIMENSION CLASSES AT AGE 34 YEARS

Grade of thinning	Breast-height diameter class					
	<12 cm		12–20 cm		>20 cm	
	m³/ha	%	m³/ha	%	m³/ha	%
A	98	22	296	67	50	11
B	100	22	318	68	46	10
C	78	17	248	55	129	28
D–B	77	17	169	38	201	45
D	87	20	186	43	159	37

TABLE 1.9
THE CLAUSHOLM THINNING EXPERIMENT: CROWN HEIGHT, CROWN PER CENT AND RUNNING TAPER
AT AGE 36 (–38) YEARS

Grade of thinning	Sample trees		Crown height m	Crown per cent %	Running taper from 1·3 m to	
	d_g cm	h_L m			7·5 m mm/m	13·5 m mm/m
A	12·5	16·1	8·5	47	4·9	(7·3)
B	14·7	16·8	7·8	54	5·2	7·9
C	17·8	17·7	6·8	62	6·1	8·7
D–B	18·7	18·4	7·3	60	6·5	9·0
D	24·2	19·8	6·8	66	7·5	10·0

TABLE 1.10
THE EAST LOLLAND THINNING EXPERIMENT: CROWN HEIGHT, CROWN PER CENT, RUNNING TAPER AND
MEAN BRANCH DIAMETER AT AGE 32 YEARS.
(Measured on Thinning Trees in Two of the Blocks).

Grade of thinning	Sample trees		Crown height m	Crown per cent %	Running taper from 1·3 m to		Mean branch diameter at 7·5 m mm
	d_g cm	h_L m			7·5 m mm/m	13·5 m mm/m	
B	10·5	13·1	8·6	34	6·0		13·9
C	15·6	16·1	7·0	57	6·3	9·0	17·6
D–B	18·2	16·8	5·6	67	7·3	10·0	20·2
D	18·7	16·5	5·4	67	7·7	10·6	19·8

TABLE 1.11
THE CLAUSHOLM THINNING EXPERIMENT: SUMMARY OF
THE STUMP DESCRIPTIONS OF ALL FELLED TTREES

Grade of thinning	Number of trees examined	Distribution of thinnings on grades of severity		
		No symptoms %	Stained wood %	Decayed wood %
THE PERIOD A. 1954/63 (19–28 YEARS)				
B	869	51	44	5
C	1324	74	20	6
D–B	1239	73	25	2
D	1242	64	33	3
THE PERIOD A. 1965/73 (30–38 YEARS)				
A	198	22	64	14
B	323	27	57	16
C	264	34	38	28
D–B	114	42	43	15
D	201	36	53	11

TABLE 1.12
THE EAST LOLLAND THINNING EXPERIMENT:
RESULTS OF THE STUMP DESCRIPTION OF ALL FELLED
TREES

Grade of thinning	Number of trees examined	Distribution of thinnings on grades of severity		
		No symptoms %	Stained wood %	Decayed wood %
THE PERIOD A. 1960/64 (21–25 YEARS)				
B	686	78	22	–
C	2092	77	22	1
D–B	2157	77	23	–
D	2395	77	22	1
THE PERIOD A. 1966/69 (27–30 YEARS)				
B	681	48	49	3
C	1099	42	52	6
D–B	583	38	58	4
D	652	46	50	4
THE PERIOD A. 1971/73 (32-34 YEARS)				
B	348	31	63	6
C	412	26	60	14
D–B	89	22	59	19
D	323	28	56	16

Health and Stability

The butt rot frequency in the experiments was followed by a systematic description of the stump surfaces of all trees removed in thinning. The results of these assessments are, for the two experiments, represented in condensed form in Tables 1.11 and 1.12 and shown graphically in Figures 1.9 and 1.10. The rot intensity has grown steadily during the respective experimental periods, but in none of the experiments has it been possible to demonstrate any relationship of thinning intensity to rot frequency; this is inconsistent with the results from a number of other Danish and south-Swedish thinning experiments.

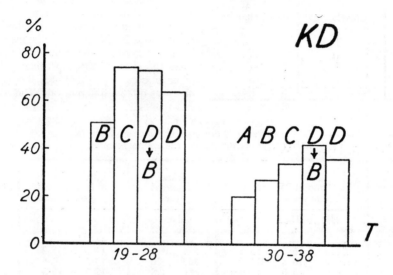

Figure 1.9 The Clausholm Experiment. Percentage of trees without butt rot in thinnings, summarised for the two age periods 19-28 and 30-38 years. T represents time in years.

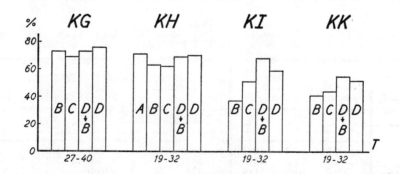

Figure 1.10 The East Lolland Experiment. Percentage of trees without butt rot in the thinning of each of the four blocks during the experimental period.

In Table 1.13 a summary survey is given of the distribution on thinning grades of the wind damages suffered during the experimental period in the two experiments; in 1967 the southern part of Denmark, where the East Lolland experiment is situated, was struck by two quite extraordinarily violent gales. As appears from the table, the number of wind-damaged trees is not very great, but there is a clear tendency for the number to increase with increasing thinning grade, and reckoned in percentages the increase becomes even heavier. It should be noted that in the East Lolland experiment particularly two of the blocks suffered heavy damage during the 1967 storms, and in both places it was the D grade that suffered most.

Both experiments have also been exposed to

TABLE 1.13

THE CLAUSHOLM AND EAST LOLLAND THINNING EXPERIMENTS: SURVEY OF WIND DAMAGE TO THE EXPERIMENTS DURING THE EXPERIMENTAL PERIOD

Grade of thinning	Number of harvested wind-damaged trees, per ha	
	Clausholm	East Lolland
A	9	18
B	11	6
C	22	19
D–B	45	24
D	44	54

snow damage; the East Lolland experiment, however, seriously in one block only. A survey of the extent and nature of the damage is given in Tables 1.14 and 1.15. In the East Lolland experiment the snow damage occurred only 5 years after the establishment of the experiment, and reckoned in percentages of the stem number the extent of the damage was approximately the same at all grades, 7 to 8%. Also the volume cut was the same, 6 to 7 cub. m per ha at all grades. In the heavy thinning grades the damage was by far the most serious.

In the Clausholm experiment, 18 years had passed since the start of the experiment when the snow damage occurred; therefore, the damage picture here was quite a different one. The A and B grades

TABLE 1.14

THE CLAUSHOLM THINNING EXPERIMENT: AN ACCOUNT OF SNOW DAMAGE OCCURRING IN THE WINTER 1971/72; 18 YEARS AFTER THE ESTABLISHMENT

Grade of thinning	Crop at 36 years before snow damage			Snow-damaged trees		Extraordinary thinning caused by snow damage		Percentage of damaged trees with stembreakage %
	N per ha	H_L m	D_g cm	Number per ha	%	D_g cm	V m³/ha	
A	3243	16·5	13·2	574	18	11·9	35·2	38
B	2378	16·8	14·5	466	20	13·1	33·6	44
C	1029	18·0	19·0	81	8	17·7	16·3	67
D–B	1019	19·1	20·4	49	5	17·7	8·0	69
D	494	19·4	23·8	7	1	23·5	3·2	100

TABLE 1.15

THE EAST LOLLAND THINNING EXPERIMENT: AN ACCOUNT OF SNOW DAMAGES OCCURRING ON ONE OF THE BLOCKS IN THE WINTER 1965/66; 5 YEARS AFTER THE ESTABLISHMENT

Grade of thinning	Crop at 27 years before snow damage			Snow-damaged trees		Extraordinary thinning caused by snow damage		Percentage of damaged trees stembreakage with %
	N per ha	H_L m	D_g cm	Number per ha	%	D_g cm	V m³/ha	
A	4157	10·4	10·7	358	9	8·0	5·4	36
B	3826	10·8	11·0	287	8	9·6	7·3	48
C	2717	10·9	11·9	179	7	10·0	5·3	41
D–B	1735	11·5	13·1	133	8	11·3	7·1	50
D	1840	11·0	12·8	116	6	11·6	6·3	73

were those that suffered most severely, and almost to the same extent, approximately 20% of all trees being damaged; in the C grade the damage was of medium severity, and in the D–B and D grades the number of damaged trees was almost of no importance. It should, however, be added that, as appears from the tables, the stem breakage percentage increases with increasing thinning intensity.

Value Production

The profit deriving from the thinnings has been calculated on the basis of the directly ascertained distribution on assortment classes of the thinning yield of each parcel in the experiments. As might be expected, by far the largest quantities of sawlog material were produced in the more heavily thinned grades; by way of example it may be mentioned that in the C, D–B and D grades of the Clausholm experiment 26, 25 and 47%, respectively, of the total thinning volume was cut as saw timber, against only 9% in the B grade. The valuation was based on the cost of labour and the selling prices in force in autumn 1973, and the calculations were made partly without interest, partly at a rate of interest of 5% (discounted back to the time of planting).

TABLE 1.16
THE CLAUSHOLM THINNING EXPERIMENT: FINANCIAL YIELD OF THE FIVE THINNING GRADES
AT AGE 38 YEARS

(The price level of autumn 1973 has been applied).

Grade of thinning	Net-on-stump value of the production at age 38 years							Capital value	
	Thinnings		Remaining crop		Total			Capital value	
	D.kr./ha	rel.	D.kr./ha	rel.	D.kr./ha	rel.		D.kr./ha	rel.
WITHOUT INTEREST									
A	1718	32	31107	109	32825	97		16025	93
B	5313	100	28657	100	33970	100		17170	100
C	12913	243	30554	107	43467	128		26667	155
D–B	12042	227	39343	137	51385	151		34585	201
D	24318	458	30848	108	55166	162		38366	223
RATE OF INTEREST 5%									
A	327	26	5372	109	5699	92		—5265	
B	1253	100	4949	100	6202	100		—4762	
C	3424	273	5277	107	8701	140		—2263	
D–B	3574	285	6794	137	10368	167		—596	
D	6259	500	5327	108	11586	187		622	

TABLE 1.17
THE EAST LOLLAND THINNING EXPERIMENT: FINANCIAL YIELD OF THE FIVE THINNING GRADES
AT AGE 34 YEARS

(The price level of autumn 1973 has been applied).
(Each treatment is represented by four parcels).

Grade of thinning	Net-on-stump value of the production at age 34 years							Capital value	
	Thinnings		Remaining crop		Total			Capital value	
	D.kr./ha	rel.	D.kr./ha	rel.	D.kr./ha	rel.		D.kr./ha	rel.
WITHOUT INTEREST									
A	68	3	25474	103	25542	95		10542	89
B	1996	100	24807	100	26803	100		11804	100
C	6579	330	23455	95	30034	112		15034	127
D–B	6915	346	26296	106	33211	124		18210	154
D	9748	488	19950	80	29698	111		14698	125
RATE OF INTEREST 5%									
A	23	4	6013	103	6036	94		—4557	
B	547	100	5887	100	6434	100		—4159	
C	1991	364	5554	95	7545	117		—3048	
D–B	2254	412	6241	106	8495	132		—2098	
D	3000	548	4791	80	7791	121		—2802	

The results from the two experiments have been represented in Tables 1.16 and 1.17, where the values are stated in Danish kroner and in relative figures, the yield of the B thinning being fixed at 100. It will be seen that in the respective experimental periods the D thinning has in both experiments yielded by far the greatest net revenue both with and without interest; without interest the C and D–B thinnings yielded about the same net revenue, but with interest the D–B thinning is superior.

On the basis of the distribution on dimensions, the value of the standing crop at the time of the assessment (the realisation value) was calculated; the results are shown in absolute and relative figures in Tables 1.16 and 1.17, without interest as well as discounted back to the time of planting at a rate of interest of 5%. It is conspicuous that in both experiments the stand in the D–B grade has the highest value, while the A grade has the second highest; however, in the Clausholm experiment the difference between the A, C and D grades is insignificant.

By adding the realisation value of the stand to the profit from the thinnings we arrive at the value of productions of the thinning grades at the ages when the last assessment was made; these amounts, too, are represented in Tables 1.16 and 1.17. In the Clausholm experiment we find at age 38 years with or without interest a rising value production with an increasing thinning intensity, and the superiority of the heavily thinned grades is most marked when interest is added; it appears that

the D–B grade is much superior to the C grade in value yield. In the East Lolland experiment, the D–B thinning at an average age of 34 years had the highest value production both with and without interest; the C and D grades had, excluding interest, very nearly the same value yield, while the D grade yielded most when interest was taken into account.

The value production of the thinning grades in the two experiments is, moreover, represented graphically in Figures 1.11 and 1.12. Figure 1.11 shows for the Clausholm experiment not only the value production in the 5 grades at 38 years, but also at the ages 30 and 34 years, and based on the same price level. Figure 1.12 shows the value yield of the thinning grades in each of the four blocks of the East Lolland experiment at the average age of 34 years.

Finally, the capital values, also shown in Tables

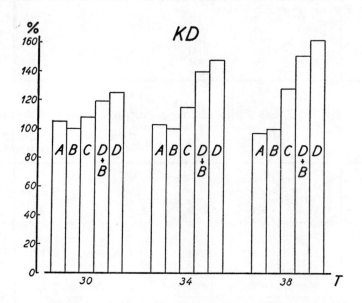

Figure 1.11 The Clausholm Experiment. Financial yield of the five thinning grades at the ages of 30, 34 and 38 years, expressed as a percentage of the B grade yield. T = time in years.

1.16 and 1.17, were calculated on the basis of cultivating costs and overheads from the accounts published by the Danish Forest Society, 6000 Dkr/ha and 300 Dkr/ha per year, respectively. Here the heavy thinning grades show themselves economically even better compared with no thinning or light thinning. In the Clausholm experiment the capital values of the D and D–B grades at rate of interest 5% are very close to nil, which implies an internal

financial yield at age 38 years of about 5% in these treatments.

In conclusion attention should be drawn to the fact that none of the ages at which data were collected for the calculations reported here are realistic rotation ages for Norway spruce in Denmark even in the best of site classes. In localities like East Lolland, however, Norway spruce often does not exceed the age of about 40 years.

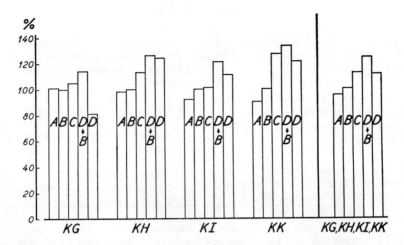

Figure 1.12 The East Lolland Experiment. Financial yield of the five thinning grades in each of the four blocks at age 32 and 40 years respectively and for the average (right) of each treatment expressed as a percentage of the B grade yield.

REFERENCES

BORNEBUSCH, C. H. (1933). Et Udhugningsforsøg i Rødgran. (Ein Durchforstungsversuch in Fichte). *Forstl.Forsøgsv. Danm.* 13.

BORNEBUSCH, C. H. (1937). Stormskaden i Hastrup Plantage den 8de Februar 1934. (Sturmschaden in dem Hastruper Durchforstungsversuch). *Forstl. Forsøgsv. Danm.* 14.

BRYNDUM, H. (1964). Forsøgsvaesenets afsluttede rødgranprøveflader. (Terminated Sample Plots in Norway spruce). *Forstl.Forsøgsv. Danm.* 28.

BRYNDUM, H. (1967). Ein Durchforstungsversuch in einem jungen Fichtenbestand. *Mitt. Forstl. Bundes-Versuchsanst. Wien.* 77.

BRYNDUM, H. (1969). Rødgranhugstforsøget i Gludsted plantage. (A Thinning Experiment in Norway spruce in Gludsted Plantation). *Forstl.Forsøgsv. Danm.* 32.

BRYNDUM, H. (1974). Rødgranhugstforsøget på Ravnholt. (A Thinning Experiment in Norway spruce at Ravnholt Forest Estate). *Forstl.Forsøgsv. Danm.* 34.

HENRIKSEN, H. A. (1961). A Thinning Experiment with Sitka spruce in Nystrup Dune Forest. *Forstl. Forsøgsv. Danm.* 27.

MØLLER, C. M. (1933). Boniteringstabeller og bonitetsvise Tilvaekstoversigter for Bøg, Eg og Rødgran i Danmark. *Dansk Skovforen. Tidsskr.* 18.

DISCUSSION

Kramer: Was branch thickness considered in calculating prices?

Bryndum: No, but branch thickness did not in any case exceed 20 mm and would consequently have little influence on either quality or price.

Kramer: Did the wind damage occur immediately after thinning or sometime later?

Bryndum: It occurred seven years after thinning. You would not expect very much damage after such a long time, as you would do if the windblow occurred immediately after thinning.

EFFECTS OF LINE THINNING ON INCREMENT

By G. J. HAMILTON

Forestry Commission, Alice Holt, Farnham, Surrey, England

Introduction

Almost irrespective of the methods employed in harvesting, line thinning has a number of advantages over selective thinning, which are fairly well understood. In the first place the need for marking the trees to be removed is more or less dispensed with. Secondly, it is usually unnecessary to undertake the intensity of brashing which would be required for selective thinning and hence the costs of this operation are either reduced or eliminated. The third advantage is that line thinning facilitates tree felling operations. Fourthly, it improves general access to the crop and usually assists extraction.

With mechanised extraction methods the last two attributes of line thinning become of even greater significance. As machines tend to get larger, so the need for more 'room to manoeuvre' becomes greater. Added to this, it is particularly the case with expensive machinery – although applying generally whatever the harvesting methods employed – that the cost of harvesting per unit volume is generally reduced as the yield per hectare, ie the weight of thinning, increases. One way of accommodating these pressures for manoeuvrability and increased yield per hectare would be to adopt heavy line thinnings, perhaps involving the removal of two or more adjacent lines, in the case of first thinnings.

No single thinning operation should be considered in isolation however, since its effect can influence the development of the crop for the rest of its life. In order to make a rational appraisal of any one thinning it is therefore necessary to consider both short and long term effects, whether beneficial or otherwise. This paper is confined to the consideration of one of these effects, namely the effect of the various forms of line thinning on the increment of the remaining crop.

Line thinnings are neutral in type, ie the distribution by dominance or size classes of the trees removed is the same as that of the trees remaining. With selective thinnings a greater proportion of the larger dominants and co-dominants are invariably retained. The first effect on increment to be considered is that resulting from the absence of positive selection of the remaining crop.

The effect of intensity of thinning, or in this case the weight of an individual thinning, is of interest in any kind of thinning. However, in line thinnings particularly, a given weight may be constituted in diverse ways. For example, the removal of half of the volume of the crop at first thinning may be effected by removing every second row, or by removing two adjacent rows in every four, or by removing three adjacent rows in every six. Clearly, the structure of the remaining crop is significantly different in each treatment. The effect on increment of these different means of removing a given weight of thinning is the second aspect of increment to be considered here.

The distribution of volume increment between individual trees, or rows of trees, resulting from line thinning is relevant in that it influences the increase in the value of the stand. This is the third aspect of increment to be considered in this paper.

The Forestry Commission has five experiments embracing line thinning treatments and it is intended to explore the evidence that is so far available from these experiments. At this point in time they have not all yielded complete information. All of the experiments are concerned with first thinnings only.

Experimental Evidence

GLENTROOL (SOUTH SCOTLAND)

This experiment was established in October 1967 in 20-year old Sitka spruce (*Picea sitchensis*) of Yield Class 17, initially spaced at 1.52×1.52 m. The site is relatively sheltered; it has a 5° slope with an east/south aspect; elevation 120 m; rainfall 1520 mm/annum; solid geology Ordovician; soil imperfectly drained brown earth.

The experiment consists of three line thinning treatments plus one selective thinning, all of which were carried out at the time of establishment of the experiment. In each treatment one-third of the volume of the standing crop was removed in thinning. The treatments were as follows:

    i. Removal of $\frac{1}{3}$ of the volume selectively – 3 replications

    ii. Removal of 1 row in 3 (leaving 2 adjacent) – 3 replications

    iii. Removal of 2 rows in 6 (leaving 4 adjacent) – 3 replications

    iv. Removal of 3 rows in 9 (leaving 6 adjacent) – 2 replications

All trees in each plot have been girthed annually since the date of establishment and a full measurement, ie measurement of total *volume production*, was made at the end of six growing seasons, ie at the end of 1973. Owing to the emergence of certain increment patterns in basal area, the crop was sampled such that volume increments could be assigned to the remaining individual rows in the crop. A second thinning was carried out in each plot at the end of 1973, but these treatments lie outside the scope of this paper.

The effect of the various treatments on the total volume increment per hectare is shown in Table 2.1. The periodic increments between the time of first thinning and the full assessment in 1973 are tabulated in column 2. These show the average for the 3 (or 2) plots in each treatment.

The absolute volume increment figures given in column 2 are, of course, directly useful but it is

TABLE 2.1

Treatment (1)	Volume increment in m³/ha from 1967–1973 (2)	Initial volume after thinning in m³/ha in 1967 (3)	Volume increment as a percentage of initial volume (4)
Third of the volume removed selectively	173·6	97·4	178·2
1 row in 3	172·9	105·57	163·8
2 rows in 6	158·6	98·6	160·9
3 rows in 9	145·6	91·85	158·6

apparent from the entries in column 3 that there were differences in initial volume stocking of the different treatments after thinning in 1967. In particular, the 1 in 3 treatment has a higher initial volume than average, whilst the 3 in 9 treatment is somewhat lower than average. It is not possible to ascertain from the data precisely how initial stocking affects the subsequent increment, nor is it suggested that the entries in column 4 can be regarded as conveying the real relativities if the initial stocking had been identical in each plot. Since it is equally unlikely that the volume increment is directly proportional to the initial volume, the real situation probably lies somewhere between the two, and a survey of the individual plot data tends to suggest that a more appropriate entry for column 2 for the 1 in 3 treatment would be somewhere in the region of 165 to 167 and for the 3 in 9 treatment the appropriate value would be closer to 150 than 145.

Taking first the question of the neutral thinning as against selective thinning, the most appropriate comparison is the selective thinning and the 1 row in 3 treatment. Allowing for the greater initial volume in the 1 row in 3 treatment, the results suggest that volume increment is greater with selective thinning, perhaps amounting to 6–8m³/ha over a 6-year period.

The next point of interest concerns the differences in increment resulting from greater numbers of adjacent rows removed. There is clearly a steady drop in increment as the width of the lane created by line thinnings becomes wider. Again, allowing for initial stocking differences the suggestion is that over a 6-year period the difference between the 1 row in 3 treatment and the 2 rows in 6 treatment is in the

order of 8 m³/ha and a similar difference is evident between the 2 rows in 6 and 3 rows in 9 treatment.

Figure 2.1 shows the average volume increment in each row expressed as a percentage of the initial volume in the row, over the 6-year period. It is clear that the response to thinning is virtually confined to the rows immediately adjacent to those removed. Very little response is discernable in the other rows, although the absence of an unthinned control in this particular experiment denies an assertion that the central rows of the 3 in 9 treatment have remained absolutely without response. Comparison of these rows with the rows 2 and 5 suggest however, that any response must be minimal. Another notable feature is that the response of the outside rows increases with the number of adjacent rows removed. Basal area responses are incidentally proportionately greater than those of the volume increment responses. Lower form factors are induced on the trees of the outside rows relative to the inside rows. The pattern of basal area response is established immediately following thinning and remains more or less constant over the 6-year period.

MILLBUIE BLACK ISLE FOREST (NORTH SCOTLAND)
This experiment was designed to compare two different forms of systematic thinning and different thinning cycles with selective thinnings. The experiment is in a stand of Scots pine, Yield Class 10, planted at a spacing of 1·4 m × 1·4 m in 1939. The experiment is situated on an irregular 2½° slope with a north-west aspect; rainfall 760 mm/annum; elevation 195 m; peaty ironpan soil overlying Old Red Sandstone. There are nine treatments in the

GLENTROOL

DISTRIBUTION OF VOLUME INCREMENT BY ROWS

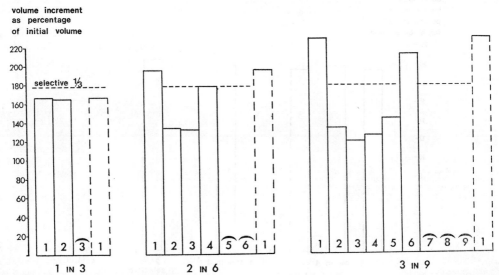

Figure 2.1

experiment, each with two replications, but since the time of first thinning has been delayed in some of the treatments there are only three treatments which have so far yielded information which is relevant to this paper. The experiment was established in April, 1966, when thinning of three of the treatments was carried out. These are:

   i. Removal of 1 row in 4

   ii. Removal of every 4th tree in every row

   iii. Removal of 25% of the stand volume selectively

These treatments were fully assessed in 1970 after the passage of four growing seasons. During the same period three other treatments remained unthinned, providing six, in effect, control plots. The total volume increment per hectare for each of these treatments is given in Table 2.2.

TABLE 2.2

Treatment	Volume increment in m³/ha from 1966 to 1970	Initial volume in m³/ha after thinning	Volume increment as a percentage of initial volume
Removal of 1 row in 4	47·3	90·8	52·0
Removal of every 4th tree	53·8	93·0	58·0
Removal of 25% volume selectively	56·0	112·1	50·0
Unthinned	59·5	125·6	47·4

In this case it is difficult to draw any definite conclusions from the evidence. Although the absolute volume increment in the selectively thinned treatments is greater than in the line thinned, the initial stocking in these plots is slightly higher. The initial stocking levels are very similar within each treatment, of which there are only two plots, and it is therefore difficult to deduce the effect of initial stocking on subsequent increment. The differences between the

1 row in 4 and 1 tree in 4 treatments are not significant.

The distribution of increment between rows in the line thinned treatment is once more of considerable interest. The basal area increment percentages over the 4 growing seasons are shown, relative to the other treatments, in Figure 2.2. In this case the centre row has shown a very small response to the thinning when compared with the unthinned control.

MILLBUIE

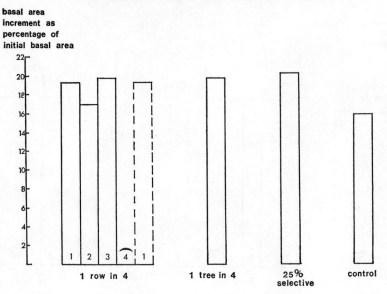

Figure 2.2

KING'S, THETFORD FOREST (EAST ENGLAND)
This experiment was established in 1970 in a stand of Corsican pine (*Pinus nigra* var *maritima*) planted in 1951 at a spacing of 1·4 m × 1·4 m and of Yield Class 18. The site is virtually level and sheltered; elevation 22 m; rainfall 640 mm per annum; soil is a brown calcimorphic on Breckland sand overlying chalky till. There are seven treatments, including an unthinned control, replicated three times.

    i. Removal of 1 row in every 3 (leaving 2 adjacent), 33⅓% volume removed
    ii. Removal of 1 row in 2 (leaving 1 row), 50% volume removed
   iii. Removal of 2 rows in every 4 (leaving 2 adjacent), 50% volume removed

    iv. Removal of 3 rows in every 5 (leaving 2 adjacent), 60% volume removed
    v. Removal of 2 rows in every 3 (leaving 1 row), 66⅔% volume removed
   vi. Removal of 3 rows in every 4 (leaving 1 row), 75% volume removed
  vii. Unthinned control

The basal area in each plot has been assessed annually since the experiment was established. A complete measurement was carried out at the end of 1974. There is no selective thinning treatment incorporated in the experiment and so this aspect of increment cannot be explored here.

The volume increment between 1970 and 1974 (5 growing seasons) is tabulated below.

TABLE 2.3

Treatment	Volume in m³/ha increment between 1970/1974	Intitial volume after thinning in m³/ha	Volume increment as a percentage of initial volume
Unthinned control	106·3	205·6	51·7
Removal of 1 row in 3	97·8	141·8	69·0
Removal of 1 row in 2	98·0	105·5	92·8
Removal of 2 rows in 4	94·5	101·7	92·9
Removal of 3 rows in 5	81·7	84·3	96·9
Removal of 2 rows in 3	80·7	69·4	116·3
Removal of 3 rows in 4	57·5	47·8	120·3

The above figures indicate that in these treatments, as the weight of thinning increases so the production decreases. Maximum production is obtained in the unthinned control and the lowest production is obtained in the 3 in 4 treatments. It is also notable when comparing the two 50% volume removal treatments that the volume production of the 1 row removed in 2 exceeds that of the 2 rows

from 4, ie the larger the gap created in line thinning the lower is the increment for the same weight of thinning.

The distribution of increment between rows is shown in Figure 2.3. Once again it is demonstrated that the response of individual rows is increased markedly with the width of the adjacent "gap".

KING'S

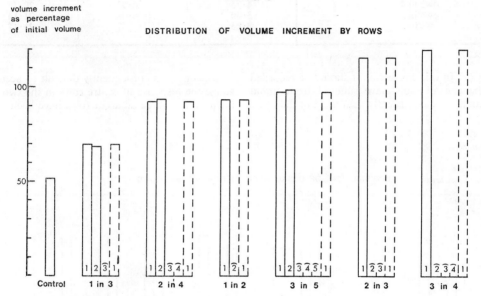

volume increment
as percentage
of initial volume

DISTRIBUTION OF VOLUME INCREMENT BY ROWS

Figure 2.3

ELWY, CLWYD FOREST (NORTH WALES)

This experiment was established in 1971 in Sitka spruce (*Picea sitchensis*) established at a spacing of 1·5 m × 1·5 m in 1952 and of Yield Class 22. The site is approximately level; elevation 259 m; moderately exposed; rainfall 762 mm/annum; brown earth soil overlying Silurian. There are eight treatments with three replications each. These are:

  i. Unthinned control
  ii. Removal of 1 row in every 4 (leaving 3 adjacent), 25% volume removed
  iii. Removal of 1 row in every 3 (leaving 2 adjacent), 33% volume removed
  iv. Removal of 2 rows in every 5 (leaving 3 adjacent), 40% volume removed
  v. Removal of 1 row in 2 (leaving 1 row), 50% volume removed
  vi. Removal of 2 rows in every 4 (leaving 2 adjacent), 50% volume removed

  vii. Removal of 3 rows in every 5 (leaving 2 adjacent), 60% volume removed
  viii. Removal of 2 rows in every 3 (leaving 1 row), 67% volume removed

The basal area of each plot has been assessed annually since establishment, which to date means that the production of only three growing seasons has been assessed. Unfortunately, the experiment has suffered an attack by *Elatobium abietinum* (Green spruce aphid) which has caused irregular defoliation over at least two growing seasons, throughout the experiment. This attack has clearly affected increment in many of the plots and consequently devalued the data collected so far. Table 2.4 contains basal area increment data for the period of three growing seasons.

Given the circumstances it is considered unwise to draw any refined conclusions from the results. The distribution of increment between rows is shown in

TABLE 2.4

Treatment	Periodic basal area increment from 1971/74 in m²/ha	Initial basal area in m²/ha after thinning	Basal area increment as a percentage of initial basal area
Unthinned control	4·73	39·53	11·97
Removal of 1 row in 4	4·92	30·46	16·15
Removal of 1 row in 3	4·74	27·15	17·46
Removal of 2 rows in 5	4·73	24·16	19·58
Removal of 1 row in 2	4·90	20·55	23·84
Removal of 2 rows in 4	4·35	20·93	20·78
Removal of 3 rows in 5	3·40	16·08	21·14
Removal of 2 rows in 3	2·83	13·37	21·17

Figure 2.4. In this connection it should be recorded that the control plots have suffered from aphid infestation more consistently than most of the other treatments. It is consequently difficult to accurately gauge the response of centre rows in the two treatments where three adjacent rows have been left.

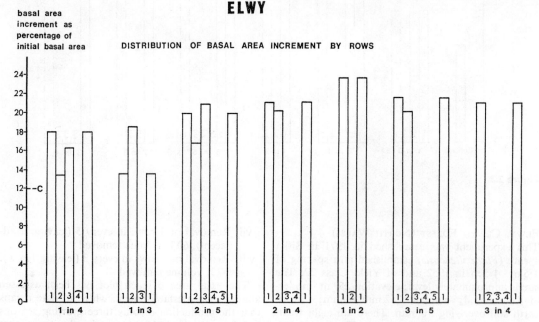

Figure 2.4

DOWNHAM, THETFORD FOREST (EAST ENGLAND)
This experiment was established in 1943 in 19-year old Corsican pine at a time when line thinnings were first carried out in this country. The site is relatively level at an elevation of 18 m and is relatively sheltered; rainfall 635 mm per annum; sandy soil overlying chalk.

Unfortunately, the experiment is not replicated and in addition suffers from the lack of a conven-

tional unthinned control. There are only 3 treatments, one plot of each:—

ii. Removal of 50% of the volume selectively
ii. Removal of 2 adjacent rows in every 4
iii. Removal of 3 adjacent rows in every 6

For each of the first three years after thinning the volume was accurately assessed in each treatment. A further assessment was made six years after thinning, but owing to deficiencies in sampling, the volume assessments were unreliable so that only basal area increments are shown for the six year period in the table below:

Top heights were clearly similar at the time of first thinning, suggesting no major site differences. The selective thinning treatment emerges clearly as having produced greater increment than either of the line thinning treatments. In this case however,

TABLE 2.5

Treatment	Top height at first thinning m	Volume increment over 3 growing seasons after thinning in m³/ha	Volume increment as percentage of initial volume	Basal area increment over 6 growing seasons after thinning in m²/ha	Basal area increment as percentage of initial basal area
50% selective	9·0	49·1	65·1	16·25	87·1
2 rows in 4	9·1	40·1	46·4	14·11	57·4
3 rows in 6	9·0	39·2	47·1	13·48	55·6

the differences are presumably a combination of the effects of the neutral thinning and the effects of creating a sizeable gap in the canopy by removing at least 2 adjacent rows. Although the relative production of the two line thinnings are in the expected order, the magnitude of the differences appears to be rather small.

The now familiar pattern of the distribution of basal area increment by rows is demonstrated in Figure 2.5 echoing the experience of the other experiments.

Discussion

The first aspect of line thinning to be discussed, in the light of experimental evidence, concerns the effect of removing trees of all dominance classes in

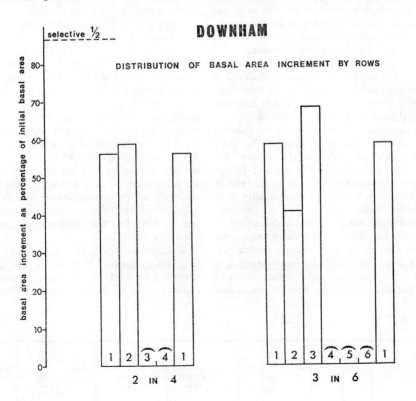

DOWNHAM

DISTRIBUTION OF BASAL AREA INCREMENT BY ROWS

Figure 2.5

line thinning as opposed to selective thinning in which a greater proportion of the better dominants and co-dominants are retained. The evidence from Glentrool and from Thetford (Downham) tends to indicate that some loss in production follows such neutral thinnings, probably in the order of 3–8 m³ in a normal thinning cycle depending on species and thinning treatments. The evidence from Millbuie is not clear. This general trend is a reasonable expectation given that in general the more efficient producers in a stand are those of greater dominance. (Hamilton 1969).

The second aspect is the question of the weight of thinning and subsequent volume increment and, at least in the more extreme treatments, it would appear that the volume increment is negatively correlated with the weight of a single thinning. However, it is much more relevant in practice to consider the effect of the pattern rather than simply the weight of thinning. The expectation here is that the removal of two or three adjacent rows would create such gaps in the canopy that the remaining trees could not sufficiently respond in order to utilise the site fully, whereas those parts of the stand which are unaffected by the treatment are losing the opportunity of diameter and hence value increment gains. This is indeed borne out by the evidence particularly from the Glentrool and Kings experiments which show greater losses in increment with increased numbers of adjacent rows removed.

One clear feature that has emerged from the experiments is that the zone of influence of thinning is very limited and there is little evidence that there is any sizeable response in rows which are not immediately adjacent to the rows removed.

Regarding the effects of line thinning on quality, there are no apparent differences between the three treatments at Thetford (Downham) but here the effects have been wholly masked by pruning. Under more extreme treatments, as with any other type of thinning, there will be a risk of poorer quality in at least a proportion of the crop.

In order to explore the economic implications of the above evidence, yield models have been constructed for a number of line thinning treatments. The scope for modelling line thinning treatments is unlimited, particularly when considering chevron patterns of removal. However, only conventional

treatments which are thought to have a bearing on field practice have been considered here. Models have been constructed for two species, Corsican pine and Sitka spruce. The first thinning treatments considered have been:

  1 row removed in 4
  1 row removed in 3
  1 row removed in 2
  2 adjacent rows removed in 4
  2 adjacent rows removed in 5

It has been assumed that subsequently the models have been thinned selectively according to normal Forestry Commission practice (Hamilton & Christie 1971). In effect this has meant that the average volume stocking in each of the treatments has subsequently been approximately the same at any given age. A yield class of 18 has been assumed. Initial stockings were 3860 and 3250 stems per hectare for Corsican pine and Sitka spruce respectively. The models have been constructed to incorporate volume losses broadly suggested by the experimental evidence. Relative to selective thinning the volume losses assumed are:

	Corsican pine	Sitka spruce
Selective	0	0
1 row in 4	5 m³/ha	6 m³/ha
1 row in 3	7 m³/ha	8 m³/ha
1 row in 2	8 m³/ha	10 m³/ha
2 rows in 5	10 m³/ha	14 m³/ha
2 rows in 4	12 m³/ha	18 m³/ha

The standard Forestry Commission methods of economic appraisal have been employed. This means that a standard (high) stumpage price/size curve has been applied to the revenues of all thinnings and fellings and discounted at a rate of 5% compound interest to the year of first thinning, ie 20 years from planting in the case of Sitka spruce, 19 years for Corsican pine. The price/size curve assumes an average harvesting cost per unit volume and makes no allowance for the effect of different thinning methods on harvesting costs. Relative to normal selective thinnings the maximum discounted revenues per hectare for the different treatments are as shown in Table 2.6.

Clearly, any form of line thinning reduces the discounted revenue relative to selective thinning, using the methods of comparison described above. However, since no account has been taken of

TABLE 2.6

	Selective	1/4	1/3	1/2	2/5	2/4
Corsican pine	0	—£92	—£98	—£91	—£110	—£110
Sitka spruce	0	—£86	—£94	—£95	—£122	—£140

differences in harvesting costs the above figures do not make the comparison wholly valid. The volume removed in the 1 row in 3 treatment is similar to that removed in the selectively thinned model. The difference in discounted revenue between the two amounts to approximately £94–£98/ha. Given a volume of removal approximately 63m³ per hectare then a saving of approximately £1·50 per cubic metre in harvesting costs must be achieved in order to justify this treatment in crops such as described here. Of course there may be further gains in harvesting costs at subsequent thinnings to be considered, as a result of easier access in the line thinning treatment.

In comparing the treatments involving single row removal there are no large differences in the discounted revenues indicated above. Although felling costs may be similar in each treatment, higher yields per hectare should normally effect a reduction in harvesting costs per unit volume which will favour the 1 row in 2 treatment and diminish the relative merits of the 1 row in 4 treatment. Treatments involving the removal of 2 adjacent rows show up least favourably in the above comparison. It is not unreasonable to expect some reduction in harvesting costs in these treatments compared with the single row removal treatments.

The above comparisons have been drawn between a number of conventional line thinning treatments and selective thinnings all planted at conventional spacings. Of course there are numerous other possible treatments, including chevron thinning, combinations of line and selective thinning, and different original planting spacings. The results which have emerged from the conventional line thinning experiment could relatively easily be applied to chevron thinnings. Where a combination of line thinning and selective thinning is used then it follows that the higher the element of selective thinning used the greater will be the revenue calculated on the basis described above. Once more the problem is one of setting this increased revenue against any possible increases in harvesting costs which result from such treatments. Where the spacing between rows is greater than normal, ie 1·8 m, then the volume losses associated with line thinnings, particularly where two adjacent rows are removed, may be greater than indicated above. Consequently, the loss in revenue can be expected to be greater than is suggested here.

Conclusions

To summarise the conclusions from the experimental evidence it might be said that:

 a. a loss of production is associated with the neutral thinning type implicit in line thinning,

 b. the zone of influence of line thinning is largely confined to the rows immediately adjacent to those removed,

 c. the response of outside rows rises markedly as the number of adjacent rows removed increases, and,

 d. greater losses in volume production are associated with greater numbers of adjacent rows removed.

Specific recommendations about line thinning treatments are not possible without considering both the harvesting system to be used and the harvesting costs which will result. As a result of economic analyses of various yield models depicting selective and line thinning treatments, some indication is given of the savings in harvesting costs required to justify the choice of one treatment in preference to others.

REFERENCES

HAMILTON, G. J. (1969). The dependence of volume increment of individual trees on dominance, crown dimensions and competition. *Forestry* 42(2).

HAMILTON, G. J. and CHRISTIE, J. M. (1971). *Forest Management Tables* Bklt 34. For. Comm. Lond. (HMSO).

DISCUSSION

Kramer: The data for the Downham plots show the relative increments only three years after thinning. Is it not so that over a much longer period these differences disappear?

Hamilton: The subsequent thinning of the plots has not been consistent in the three treatments and so it is not possible to distinguish between the effects of the first thinning and the effects of the subsequent thinning. As far as the other experiments are concerned I do not expect the volume production differences between treatments to diminish over a longer period. I see no reason why they should.

Stratmann: Did you notice any consistent increment pattern emerging regarding the geographical orientation of the rows after thinning?

Hamilton: The diagrams were drawn with this point in mind. In Glentrool, for example, the rows run approximately east and west (so that the left hand margin in Figure 2.1 represents south). You can see that there appears to be a greater overall response on the edge rows which face south, although this pattern is not consistent in each individual plot within a treatment.

Paper 3

YIELD AND DEVELOPMENT OF UNTHINNED NORWAY SPRUCE STANDS IN WESTERN NORWAY

By OLA BØRSET

Department of Silviculture, Agricultural College of Norway, Ås

Current economic trends in Norway, characterised by a marked increase in wages and social costs have greatly affected our silvicultural practice. One of the results is that an ever-larger part of the annual cut is taken out by clear-fellings. While in the 1930's, it was commonly considered advantageous to take out around 50 per cent of the total yield in spruce stands by frequent thinnings, consideration is currently being given to one single, two or three thinnings per rotation and sometimes, even no thinning.

The steep terrain of West Norway causes special problems in carrying out profitable thinnings. Therefore there is now a commonly held opinion that the planting espacement – when new stands are established in such terrain – should be widened so much that the plantations can be left unthinned and the total yield harvested in a final cut at the age of 50 to 60 years.

To elucidate more closely the development of unthinned spruce plantations, the Department of Silviculture has studied 31 sample plots in different parts of western Norway. Forest Research Officer, Helge Frivold, has done the field measurements. He

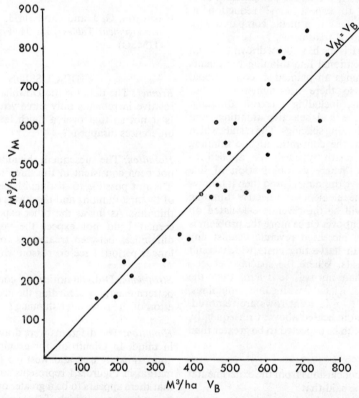

Figure 3.1 Total volume yield in sample plot (V_M) compared to total volume yield by yield tables of Brantseg (1951) at the same age and for the same site class (V_B). Sample plots at sites exceeding site classification of Brantseg are omitted.

has also written a report of the studies which will be published next year. Practical forestry has shown a considerable interest in this work.

A brief discussion of the most important results of the study is given below.

The Sample Plots

All stands examined are situated in a humid climate (annual precipitation 1500 to 3000 mm). Many lie on steep slopes with good soil. Ten plots have gradients of 50 per cent or more, another ten have gradients between 20 and 50 per cent. By the site classifications for spruce plantations in West Norway (Brantseg, 1951), twenty plots are of Site 1 or better (Site 1 – mean annual increment 14·8 m^3 after 60 years).

Yield

A remarkably large basal area of living trees was found in many plots as illustrated by the following distributions:

Basal area, living
trees (m^2 per ha)   26–50   51–75   76–100
No of plots   15   14   2

The distribution by volume per hectare is:

Volume
(m^3 per ha) 300   301–500   501–700   701
No. of
plots   5   11   10   5

The total yield in each plot has been compared to the total yield according to the yield tables of Brantseg (1951) (Successful, lightly thinned West Norwegian spruce plantations). Such a comparison is attended by some uncertainty, one of the reasons being that Brantseg's site classification is based on mean height. As may be seen from Figure 3.1 the total yield on the unthinned plots seems to be largely the same as on "Yield table plots".

Natural Thinnings

The loss from natural thinning is expressed in terms of 'death percentage', ie volume of all planted, naturally dead trees that could be observed when plots were measured, as a percentage of the total volume in the plots. This death percentage is likely to be a little lower than the natural thinning percentage but the difference is certainly small in most plots.

The distribution by death percentage is as follows:

Death
percentage   0–5   6–10   11–15   16–20   all
No. of plots 21   5   0   2   28

(3 plots omitted because of cuttings etc.)

The proportion of dead trees is remarkably small when measured by volume but it is large when expressed in terms of numbers of trees. Accordingly, the dead trees must have been suppressed early, expiring before reaching any considerable size. The more vigorous trees then presumably have been capable of establishing and strengthening their leadership even without help from thinnings. This is probably due to the very favourable climate for spruce in West Norway – high rainfall and a long growing season.

Diameter Distribution

The tree size is very important to economic results.

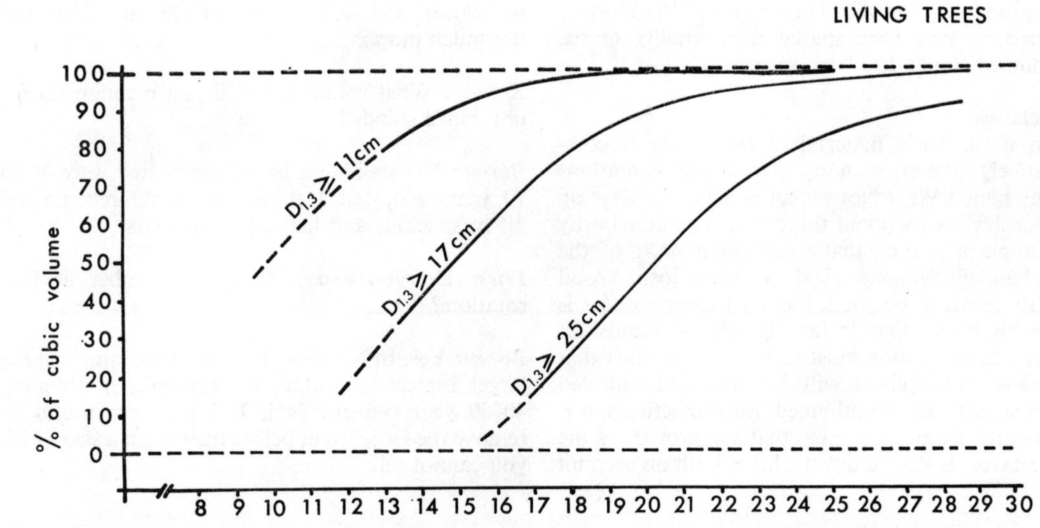

LIVING TREES

Figure 3.2   **Distribution of volume by diameter classes in relation to mean height.**

48   FORESTRY COMMISSION BULLETIN No. 55

The diameter composition is expressed by the proportion of "large trees" in a stand. "Large trees" are defined in two ways, as trees with a dbh greater than 17 and 25 cm respectively.

The following may be seen from Figure 3.2:

Mean heights exceeding 15 m at least 80 per cent by volume of living trees were large enough to yield pulpwood (dbh 11cm). At mean heights exceeding 20 m at least 80 per cent by volume were large enough to yield saw timber (dbh 17 cm). At mean heights exceeding 20 m moreover a considerable part of cubic mass consisted of trees with dbh 25 cm.

This diameter distribution has been compared to distribution tables for spruce plantations in South-East, middle and North Norway (Vestjordet, 1972). It was found that there were more large trees per hectare on the West Norwegian unthinned plots than on thinned plots at the same stage of development in other parts of Norway – where the limits for large trees were set at 17 or 25 cm. Mean diameter, however, is somewhat smaller on the unthinned plots.

The conclusion from this must be that the diameter development of the unthinned plots in West Norway has been surprisingly good and "normal". Again, we see that the most vigorous trees are fighting their way through even without help from thinnings, probably because of the favourable climate for growth.

Soundness and Stability
It sometimes happens that overstocked, unthinned stands suffer from calamities– mainly snow breaks and windthrow. But the plantations in West Norway seemed to have been spared this. Vitality of the unthinned stands has been surprisingly good.

Conclusion
Even if the basic material of this study is comparatively modest, it shows that spruce plantations in the humid West Norwegian climate can develop favourably even without thinnings. A great majority of sample plots show that a very small part of the merchantable volume yield is being lost. Wood quality seems to be good, the dry matter content is probably higher than in heavily thinned stands. Of course, consideration must be given to the fact that diameter development will be somewhat retarded when stands are left unthinned. But, sometimes, it is considered as an advantage that the growth of the largest trees is slowed down a little, both on account

of wood quality and because dimensions may be too large for the Norwegian market. However, the differences in tree dimensions within unthinned stands can be considered as disadvantageous to the economy of logging.

Altogether, a "no-thinning" forestry might be the most economical solution for difficult logging conditions in West Norway, and maybe also in coastal areas of North Norway.

REFERENCES
BRANTSEG, A. (1951). Kubikk- og produksjonsundersøkelser i vest-norske granplantninger. Summary: Investigations on volume and yield in spruce plantations in West Norway. *Meddr. Vestl. forstl. ForsStn* 9: 1–109.

VESTJORDET, E. (1972). Diameterfordelinger og høydekurver for ensaldrede granbestand. Summary: Diameter distributions and height curves for evenaged stands of Norway spruce. *Meddr. norske SkogforsVes.* 29: 469–557.

DISCUSSION
W. Sutton: You raised the question of wider spacing. How wide do you think we can go, and is there enough research on the effects of wide spacing on quality and so on?

Børset: We do not have many spacing experiments in Norway but when we put together what we have in Norway with those in Sweden, then we probably have a real programme. Those in the best position to make recommendations suggest 2·0 m×2·0 m but not closer, and we can go up to 2·5 m×2·5 m but not much more.

Kramer: What rotation would you recommend for unthinned stands?

Børset: The stands we have investigated were 40 to 70 years old, but I think we should recommend 2·5 m spacings and harvest at 50 years.

Fries: Do you expect to get sawtimber at that rotation?

Børset: Yes. In Norway at present we cannot sell the larger material, so that, for example, in thinning 40–60 year old stands it is often very useful to remove the larger trees before they reach a size which you cannot sell.

THE DEVELOPMENT OF THINNING SYSTEMS IN YOUNG SITKA SPRUCE AND CONTORTA PINE CROPS

By G. J. GALLAGHER

Forest and Wildlife Service, Department of Lands, Republic of Ireland

The predominance of young plantations of Sitka spruce (*Picea sitchensis* (Bong.) Carr.) and coastal contorta pine (*Pinus contorta* Douglas ex Loudon) in State forests of the Republic of Ireland highlights problems associated with the management of fast growing exotic conifers in an Atlantic climate. Thinning these plantations poses major difficulties.

There is little forestry tradition in the Republic. State forestry, the main enterprise, is less than 75 years old. Re-forestation was undertaken only to a limited extent until the 1950's. Since then, however, 10,000 ha have been planted annually. Most of this has been on land, not previously wooded. Over 70% of these plantations comprise Sitka spruce and almost 20% contorta pine. The lack of a forest tradition has both advantages and disadvantages. On the debit side there is a lack of long term growth and yield information, the absence of historical silvicultural lessons, and scanty information on the effects of managing forests on sites heretofore unplanted. On the credit side, this lack of tradition has meant that problems could be tackled without the inhibiting influence of deeply held classical views. In addition the need to maintain a forestry programme through the purchase of new land has increased sensitivity to economic factors.

The question of rationalising thinnings and reducing their cost is common to all countries, but the development of thinning systems in a re-afforestation programme emphasises some major problems. Rowan (1972) describes a system as a group of interdependent items that together achieve a single purpose. The search for a system which links the silvicultural and operational steps needed to produce timber cheaply from intermediate cuttings, while benefiting the remaining crop, is a continuing one. Some of the steps have been investigated in the Republic, and the extent to which these contribute to a system for Sitka spruce and contorta pine is described.

Silvicultural Aspects

Thinning practice in the Republic has until recently involved frequent and light thinnings. Various pressures have led to changes. The most important are:—

(1) The need for quick return on investment in terms of rapid diameter growth, leading to shorter rotations.

(2) The demands from wood processing industries (mainly chipboard and hardboard producers) for continued supplies of material from forests which are still young.

Plantations have been established at 3000 trees per ha and though wider spacings are now used competition between trees at an early stage means that diameter growth is slow.

One of the first aspects to be investigated was the intensity of thinning required to allow high early yields and to maintain increment. A number of experiments have been laid down since the early 1960's to deal with these questions.

TABLE 4.1

THINNING INTENSITY EXPERIMENTS

Species	Established	Age	Replications	Treatment
Sitka spruce	1964	21	3×2	3 intensities
Sitka spruce	1968	17	5×3	5 intensities
Sitka spruce	1971	18	2×3×3	3 intensities 3 fertiliser treatments
Contorta pine	1962	14	8×3	Different numbers of thinnings during rotations
Contorta pine	1962	17	8×2	Different numbers of thinnings during rotations
Contorta pine	1965	12	7×3	Different numbers of thinnings during rotations
Contorta pine	1964	17	4×2	4 intensities (all contorta pine experiments wind damaged)

Thinning Intensity

Following an analysis of early results from thinning experiments (Gallagher 1969) an examination of recent data from these experiments gives some guide lines on thinning intensity. Table 4.2 suggests that for Sitka spruce first thinnings can be moderately heavy (up to 33% standing basal area or volume removal) without increment loss. Subsequent moderately heavy thinnings (40–60% periodic basal area increment removed) may cause a small loss. Very heavy first and subsequent thinnings appear to result in some loss in increment.

TABLE 4.2

THE EFFECT OF THINNING INTENSITY ON SITKA SPRUCE

Age	LIGHT 15% BA removed 20–40% BAI removed		MODERATE 30% BA removed 40–60% BAI removed		HEAVY 45% BA removed 60–80% BAI removed	
	Volume increment (m³)					
21–25	117 (100)		121 (103)		106 (91)	
25–29	187 (100)		164 (88)		155 (83)	
	Main crop Diameters (cm)					
21	13·8 (100)		16·1 (117)		18·2 (132)	
25	16·0 (100)		18·9 (118)		21·9 (137)	
29	18·0 (100)		21·8 (121)		26·6 (148)	
	Thinnings removed					
	diam (cm)	Vol. (m³)	diam (cm)	Vol. (m³)	diam (cm)	Vol. (m³)
21	8·1 (100)	24 (100)	10·3 (127)	80 (333)	12·8 (158)	138 (575)
25	10·8 (100)	14 (100)	14·5 (134)	33 (236)	17·6 (162)	43 (307)
29	12·1 (100)	17 (100)	17·0 (140)	48 (282)	22·0 (182)	70 (412)

Brackets denote data as a % of Light Thinning.

TABLE 4.3

THE EFFECT OF THINNING INTENSITY ON CONTORTA PINE

Age	VERY LIGHT 15% BA removed	LIGHT 25% BA removed	HEAVY 38% BA removed	VERY HEAVY 45% BA removed
	Volume increment (m³)			
17–23	128 (100)	134 (105)	125 (98)	134 (105)
	Main crop Diameters at 1st and 2nd thinning (cm)			
17	12·4 (100)	11·0 (89)	12·9 (104)	12·1 (98)
23	14·2 (100)	15·1 (106)	16·1 (113)	16·0 (113)
	Volume of thinnings removed (m³)			
17	14 (100)	28 (200)	62 (443)	64 (457)
23	7 (100)	24 (342)	39 (557)	57 (814)

Brackets denote data as a % of very light thinning

The effect of the first thinnings on volume increment is reasonably consistent with the concept of a 'marginal thinning' (Bradley 1969, Hamilton and Christie 1971) though possibly after second thinning crops are more sensitive to thinning weight than expected. At this stage differences in volume increment are not statistically significant. Some recent measurements from a more extensive Sitka spruce experiment are not inconsistent with the results but require further study. The position with contorta pine seems to be less clear so far. Over a range of thinning intensities no definite trend is discernible (Table 4.3). Again there are differences in diameter measurements at 1·3 m.

The suggestion is then that while there may be some loss in Sitka spruce from very heavy first thinnings, thinnings of about 33% standing volume removal have not had a serious effect. Good volumes

can be achieved and the mean diameter increment at 1·3 m on the remaining crop is increased. This is a consideration while the very marked difference in price between pulp sized material and sawlogs operates. At a 5% interest rate a rotation producing sawlog material at 50 years might be worth twice that of a pulp rotation at 30 years. Thinnings, which involve time in selection and measurement, are costly however, and as Fries (1969) points out, costs at first thinning stage are critical.

Thinning Type

As results from thinning intensity trials began to emerge the need for the study into varying types at moderately heavy intensity was realised.

Table 4.4 lists thinning type experiments established in Sitka spruce.

The first comparisons were between various

TABLE 4.4

THINNING TYPE EXPERIMENTS IN SITKA SPRUCE

Year	Age of crop	Replications	Treatments
1963	18	2×2	Low and Scottish Eclectic
1968	17	6×2	6 types including normal low and row
1971	17	8×3	8 types including row-mechanised and semi-mechanised

selective methods. No differences worth mentioning were noted between conventional low thinning and the more complex selective Scottish Eclectic method (McDonald 1961, Gallagher 1969).

In the 1968 experiment 5 thinning types, each removing systematically 33% of standing basal area at first thinning, and, in 4 of the treatments, 25% of standing basal area removal at second thinning, were compared with conventional low thinning of the same weight.

	First	*Second*
01	Conventional low	Selection continued
02	Every 3rd tree removed	Unthinned
03	Every 3rd row removed	Every 4th row removed to leave gaps of 2 rows
04	Every 5th and 6th row removed	Every 4th row removed to leave gaps of 3 rows
05	Rows in two directions	Every 4th row removed to leave gaps of 1 row
06	Largest trees removed	Largest trees removed

Variation in increment within blocks meant that differences were not significant though, there was a slight suggestion that low thinnings did better. (Table 4.5).

Mean diameters at 1·3 m, where largest trees were removed, were reduced; also reduced were diameters at 1·3 m in rows between unthinned adjoining rows.

The second thinning was designed to increase the differences in crop structure caused by first thinning to effect differences which would more easily be detected.

TABLE 4.5

EFFECT OF THINNING TYPE ON SITKA SPRUCE

Treatment	01	02	03	04	05	06
Volume increment 1968–72 (m³) (increment as a % of 01.)	141 (100)	130 (92)	117 (82)	122 (87)	136 (96)	119 (84)

TABLE 4.6
TIME CONTENT OF THINNING TYPES (% OF CONVENTIONAL LOW THINNING)

Treatment	01	01	02	03	04	05	06
	time in minutes per plot						
F1	14·4	100	42	1	2	36	2
F2	14·5	100	49	52	47	66	73
L1	14·4	100	42	44	44	63	97
L2	14·5	100	49	52	47	66	73
L3	14·5	100	49	49	44	74	84
L4	2·2	100	217	187	145	151	241
G1	129·6	100	102	111	94	116	128
G2	227·6	100	72	92	79	89	113
G3	26·1	100	87	96	93	105	109
H1	223·7	100	147	142	161	150	200
ALL	731·5	100	86	83	76	92	112
Forester	28·9	100	46	26	24	37	38
Worker	702·6	100	96	97	88	102	131

Costings

A time study was done during the establishment of the thinning type experiment. The following elements were measured:—

F1	Selection	}	
F2	Booking	}	1 Forester
L1	Marking	}	
L2	Painting	}	1 worker
L3	Measuring	}	
L4	Volume sampling (tariff)		2 workers
*G1	Felling	}	
G2	Snedding	}	2 workers
G3	Stump protection	}	
H1	Extraction		2 workers and horse

It clearly emerged that both row thinnings by removal of every 3rd row and every 5th and 6th row were less costly than others. Removal of largest trees came next. Removal of every 3rd tree was time consuming because of trees left hanging during felling. Brashing, a very costly operation, was not listed for this study. It is obvious, however, that any form of row thinning would reduce this operation. Heavier row first thinnings are now being tried.

Harvesting

A committee was established in 1970 and given the following objectives.

1. To study all aspects of forest crop harvesting including the present practice, techniques and trends;
2. To make recommendations on harvesting techniques, engineering services and marketing.

This basically involved investigations of harvesting systems for different patterns and intensities of thinning. The emphasis was on variants of the thinning types and intensities described earlier.

These incorporated:—

(a) Shortwood row thinning methods
(b) Skylines

As Whayman (1973) points out machines and working systems cannot be considered in isolation. A fairly extensive project was undertaken to investigate thinning systems, operational methods and machines together.

Four machine methods of extraction were investigated.

(1) Tractor with pallets;
(2) Hiab loader unit;
(3) Igland winch attached to Fordson four-wheel drive;
(4) Rome guillotine.

The thinning grade comprised a systematic thinning involving removal of every 3rd row. Details are as follows:—

A. Felling, stump treatment, trimming and joining by chainsaw operator. Shortwood was stacked in 0·5 m³ piles on pallets for extraction by tractor with mounted fork lift. Pallets are 12–18 metres apart.

A1. As for A except that shortwood from three lines are thrown into the centre line. Pallets are 4–6 metres apart.

A2. As for A except that shortwood is produced from one to three trees and piled in untouched rows at right angles for extraction by Hiab loader.

B. Chain saw operator fells, treats stumps and trims. Extraction is by Igland winch attached to four wheel drive tractor.

C. Whole tree removal by 'Rome Guillotine'. Shears attachment on a standard Caterpillar 920 with split frame hydraulic powered steering.

*Felling of experimental sample trees included

TABLE 4.7

STANDARD TIMES AND COSTS FOR THINNING/EXTRACTION SYSTEMS

Thinning	Time		Cost pence/m³
	Standard Man Minutes	Standard Machine Hours	
A	98·4	6·4 (Pulp)	133
A1	107·6	6·4 (Pulp)	145
A	104·0	6·4 [85% Pulp	148
	166·0	16·2 [15% commercial lengths]	
A1	107·6	6·4 [85% Pulp	159
	166·0	16·2 [15% commercial lengths]	
A2	71·2	19·5	140
B	169·0	0·38	182
C	Method rejected because of difficulties.		

Limitations for A were twofold, (1) brashing would be required (2) Palletting proved tedious for operators. Type B did not require intensive brashing but there were problems associated with drains and fences. Type C caused considerable damage to roads and trees at the end of rows while very rapid accumulation of lop and top occurred at road edges.

Further investigations have dealt with extraction by skyline associated with row thinning and with weights of thinning varied up to 40% standing basal area removal. Direct comparisons have not been made between tractor and skyline methods, but some studies have been done to improve the skyline method by comparing lengths of racks and the distance between them. Work is also in progress to allow for an overall thinning design to suit tractor or skyline at moderately heavy intensity row thinning.

Wind Damage

Most wind damage in Sitka spruce and contorta pine plantations has been associated with gusting during severe storms when gusts of over 80 kilometres per hour were experienced. Specific investigations to associate windblow with thinning have been limited but the 1974 storms with gusting of 115 kilometres per hour did provide an opportunity to review damage in sample plots (Gallagher 1974). Table 4.8 shows that out of 64 contorta pine plots,

including unthinned plots, only 8 were undamaged and these were unthinned plots. The situation was not as severe for Sitka spruce. Of 129 plots 96 were undamaged and though the damage was greater in row or systematically thinned plots, nevertheless 40 out of 55 escaped damage.

Conclusion

Results are tenuous but do suggest that first row thinning types of moderately heavy intensity (33% standing volume removal) will be feasible for Sitka spruce. The alignment of these rows needs further investigation but the cheapness of the system is attractive. Small machines can operate these thinnings and provided the basic framework is established at first thinning, further reduction in costs will depend on technology and operations research – whether through wheel machines or winches. Large and costly machines are not now suitable for small scattered operations. Study of subsequent thinnings – with regard to crop structure and diameter assortments are required. Windthrow may pose considerable problems for contorta pine, but the range of Sitka spruce sites in the Republic suggests less difficulties with this species. The question of increased spacing has not been dealt with but will form an integral part of future studies of crop structure and thinning.

TABLE 4.8

THINNING SAMPLE PLOTS AND EXPERIMENTS DAMAGED BY WIND

Forest	Site	Species	Top Ht. Cl. (m)	T_0			T_1			T_2			T_m			T_c		
				0	1	2	0	1	2	0	1	2	0	1	2	0	1	2
Killavullen	Peaty gley podsol	PC	>15		1			3	3		3	1						
Killavullen	Peaty gley podsol	PC	>15			1			1			12						
Killavullen	Peaty gley podsol	PC	>15			1			1		1	1						
Ballynoe	Podsol	PC	10-15											5				
Ballynoe	Podsol	PC	10-15												12			
Ballynoe	Podsol	PC	>15	1			1						1					
Kilworth	Peaty podsol	PC	>15		1		3	1	2									
Rathdrum	Podsolic	PC	10-15		1			2	2									
Forth	Podsolic	PC	>15	1		1	1											
Total				2	3	3	5	6	9	–	4	14	1	5	12			
Avoca	Brown earth	SS	>15	2								1			2			1
Avoca	Gley	SS	>15				2			2			5	1				
Arigna	Gley	SS	10-15	1								1			1			
Ballyfarnan	Gley	SS	10-15	1														
Clonaslee	Peaty podsol	SS	10-15	1						1				1				
Coolgreany	Podsolic	SS	>15				2									2		
Coolgreany	Podsolic	SS	10-15				1									3		
Dromhierney	Gley	SS	10-20										1					
Drumkeeran	Gley	SS	10-15													1		
Glen Imaal	Gley	SS	>15									1						
Kinnitty	Peaty gley podsol	SS	10-15	3			6											
Kinnitty	Peaty gley podsol	SS	>15								2	2	2	1				
Kinnitty	Peaty gley podsol	SS	10-15							2	1	2						
Ossory	Peaty podsol	SS	10-15				2											
Portlaoise	Gley	SS	10-15	1			1			1								
Mountrath	Podsolic	SS	>30				2											
Mullinavat	Peaty podsol	SS	10-15	1									11	1	1			
Muskerry	Peaty podsolic	SS	10-15	6					1				10	3				
Rossmore	Peaty gley	SS	10-15	3									11	1	1			
Shillelagh	Podsolic	SS	10-15	6			9							1	1			
Total				25	–	–	25	–	1	6	3	7	40	9	6	6	–	1

T_0 No thinning
T_1 Light to moderately heavy
T_2 Heavy
T_m Systematic
T_c Crown

0 0-5% trees blown
1 5-20% trees blown
2 >20% trees blown

PC Contorta pine (Coastal)
SS Sitka spruce

REFERENCES

BRADLEY, R. T. (1969). The influence of thinning grade and thinning method on stand increment. *Proc. IUFRO meeting:Thinning and Mechanisation, Stockholm*, 108–109.

FRIES, J. (1969). Value of residual stand principal views. *Proc. IUFRO meeting. Thinning and Mechanisation. Stockholm* 21–28.

GALLAGHER, G. J. (1969). The thinning of Sitka spruce; two experiments: *Irish Forestry*, Vol. 26.1. 4–20

GALLAGHER, G. J. (1974). Windthrow in State Forests of the Republic of Ireland. *Irish Forestry*, 31, 2. 154–167.

HAMILTON, G. J. and CHRISTIE, J. M. (1971). *Forest management tables*. Booklet 34 For Comm. Lond. HMSO.

McDONALD, J. A. B. (1961). The simple rules of the Scottish Eclectic thinning method. *Scottish Forestry*, 15, 220–226.

ROWAN, A. A. (1972). Harvesting systems present and future. *Supplement to Forestry, Harvesting and marketing* 13–35. Oxford University Press.

WHAYMAN, A. (1973). Forest testing of machinery. *Work Study in Forestry*. Bull. 47. For Comm. Lond. 76–77. HMSO.

Paper 5

NEW ZEALAND EXPERIENCE WITH RADIATA PINE

By W. R. J. SUTTON*

Forest Research Institute, Rotorua, New Zealand

Although New Zealand is not the only country which relies on plantations as the major source of wood, it is probably unique in that most of its wood comes from clearfellings and not thinnings. Since thinning cannot objectively be considered independent of the total management system, and since New Zealand is probably nearer to a balanced wood supply from her plantations than any other country, her experiences in thinning may be of some relevance to this meeting.

Historical Background

At the beginning of this century it was recognised that New Zealand's indigenous forests could not provide the country's wood needs beyond the 1960s and large plantations (mainly of Radiata pine – *Pinus radiata* D. Don) were established in the late 1920s and early 1930s. It was always intended that most of these plantations would be thinned, but absence of money, the Second World War and, most important, the absence of markets meant that little or no thinning was done. By the late 1940s, stands of Radiata pine were approaching 30 m, or more, in height and 60 m²/ha, or more, basal area, and competition within the stands was intense. In the absence of any action by management, nature took the matter into her own hands, and, through the agent of the Sirex wood wasp, thinned the stands "naturally". The Sirex epidemic was certainly not the disaster with which it is generally credited in the world forestry literature. True, the losses do appear dramatic (on a good average site 450 m³/ha over 35 years – equivalent to an MAI of 13 m³/ha/yr – the total volume left was 810 m³/ha, an MAI of 23 m³/ha/yr) (Spurr, 1962) but losses were usually confined to small lower dominance trees and growth was concentrated on to fewer stems which could be felled and utilised earlier than would have been possible without the "thinning". Clearfellings from these Sirex thinned stands now make up more than 90% of the Radiata wood supplied to New Zealand industry for export.

The experience of the Sirex epidemic demonstrated that stands must be thinned. Early conversion experience also indicated that pruning would be desirable.

The Need for Pruning

Radiata's intrinsic wood properties make it a potentially useful species for a wide range of end uses: peeling, sawtimber (both finishing and strength grades) and chipping (mechanical and chemical pulps, chipboard etc). These properties, particularly density, are not greatly affected by treatment, especially those, such as thinning, which affect the rate of growth (see Sutton and Harris, 1974). By far the most important degrading factor are the branches or, more correctly, the size, condition and distribution of the resultant knots.

Attempts to control branch size and condition by silvicultural means have largely proved unsuccessful or impracticable:

Attempts to restrict branch size by close initial spacing and holding stands until the non-response of the branches within the bottom 1½ to 2 log lengths can be assured has meant that first thinning must be delayed until stands are 20 m or more high. Such treatments suffer wind damage and require long rotations. The potential for restricting branch size by genetic selection appears limited (Shelbourne, 1970).

Attempts to control branch condition by maintaining deep live crowns to ensure that resultant knots would remain intergrown have also proved unsuccessful because the knots are large and because Radiata pine almost always produces whorls of branches within the green crown which die after only one season's growth.

Branch distribution is not influenced by silvicultural treatment. Sawn knotty Radiata, no matter how it is grown, is not of a high grade. Rarely would it be better than Scandinavian fifths or North American lower common's grades. Yet free of knots its grade (ignoring the restriction on ring width) could be Scandinavian firsts or North American "B" Select.

The only way to grow quality Radiata pine for peeling, finishing and strength uses is to grow it free of knots. This means pruning. (There is one other alternative – viz. grow uninodal trees from which the long clear internodes can be cut and used as such or finger-jointed – but selected seed from uninodal parents is needed first).

*Currently N.R.A.C. Post Graduate Research Fellow at Oxford University.

The First Tending Schedules

Recognising the need for thinning and pruning, and influenced by classical thinning teaching, Ure (1949) developed a schedule which incorporated pruning, early thinnings to waste and two later thinnings with yield. This was later modified to include only one thinning with yield (Penistan, 1960). Virtually the same schedule is in operation today in some forests of New Zealand. Details are given in Table 5.1.

TABLE 5.1

TENDING SCHEDULE – 'YIELD THINNING REGIME'

Mean Height Crop Trees (m)	Operation
–	Plant 2,240 stems/ha (spacing approximately $2 \cdot 4 \times 1 \cdot 8$ m)
$6 \cdot 0$	Prune 500 stems/ha 0–$2 \cdot 4$ m
$9 \cdot 1$	Prune 320 stems/ha $2 \cdot 4$–$4 \cdot 3$ m
$12 \cdot 2$	Prune 320 stems/ha $4 \cdot 3$–$6 \cdot 1$ m
$12 \cdot 2$	Thin to 500 stems/ha (no yield)
$27 \cdot 0$	Thin to 198 stems/ha (with yield)
41–46	Clearfell

In 1959–60 the first stands treated on this regime were thinned and the extracted material was sent to a sawmill. After the initial intake the sawmill refused to continue sawing because it claimed the grades were poor, conversion low and the cost of the sawing high. The cost of extracting the thinnings also proved high and the whole operation made a loss. The subject of thinning for yield has been controversial ever since.

Research on Tending and the Development of an Alternative Regime

Initial research took the form of investigations into the quality of thinnings as sawlogs, the effect of thinning on the residual stand, and the economics of the operation. When these investigations confirmed that thinning for yield may not increase overall yields, produce intermediate returns or allow greater selection of the final crop, the research effort was intensified on the development of tending regimes which did not include thinning yields.

The research approach was to study the total system, in particular: the interactions between initial spacing, pruning, thinning and the final crop; the importance of the timing and intensity of silvicultural operations; and the quality of, and price differentials for, the extracted end products.

The work indicated that pruning could greatly enhance the quality and value of the final crop but only if the pruning was severe and associated with thinnings. The quality and economics of a regime are determined primarily by the timing and intensity of the silvicultural operations.

The first proposals for an alternative regime were those for a "Short Rotation Sawlog Regime" (Fenton and Sutton, 1968) and further refinements were presented in the 'Direct Regime' (Fenton, *et al.*, 1972). Details of the regime are given in Table 5.2.

TABLE 5.2

TENDING SCHEDULE – "DIRECT REGIME"

Mean Height Crop Trees (m)	Operation
–	Plant 1,500 stems/ha (spacing approximately $3 \cdot 7 \times 1 \cdot 8$ m)
$4 \cdot 9$	Prune the best 740–620 stems/ha 0–$2 \cdot 4$ m Thin all others (no yield)
$7 \cdot 9$	Prune the best 370–320 stems/ha $2 \cdot 4$–$4 \cdot 3$ m (If incorporating grazing, thin all others)
$10 \cdot 7$	Prune the best 198 stems/ha $4 \cdot 3$–$6 \cdot 1$ m Thin all others (no yield)
$13 \cdot 7$	Prune 198 stems/ha (multinodals) $6 \cdot 1$–$8 \cdot 5$ m
$16 \cdot 8$	Prune 198 stems/ha (multinodals) $8 \cdot 5$–$11 \cdot 0$ m

The object of this regime is to maintain maximum diameter growth on the crop trees; quality being achieved by selective frequent early pruning to restrict the defect core to a minimum. Unselected trees are eliminated as early as possible because their retention is now known to restrict growth of the pruned trees (Sutton and Crowe, 1972) and because the earlier their removal the lower the cost.

With genetically superior stock even wider initial spacings are possible – 7·3 × 1·8 m are under investigation.

Comparison of the Two Regimes

The two regimes have been very fully investigated and much of the research is already published (Fenton and Sutton, 1968; Fenton *et al.*, 1972). All I have attempted to do here is to summarise the major findings under the headings proposed for this meeting. Comparisons are for the same site (good average North Island forest site).

a. *Growth and Stability*

Compared in Table 5.3 are the expected growth rates of the two regimes and, in Table 5.4, the expected extracted volumes. The rotation for the regime with a "Yield Thinning" is 36 years (with the commercial thinning at 19 years); the rotation for the "Direct" Regime is 26 years. Also in Table 5.4 are MAIs for the two regimes.

TABLE 5.3

COMPARISON OF PREDICTED GROWTH RATES

| Height (m) | Yield Thinning Regime | | | Direct Regime | | |
	Stems/ha	Basal Area (m²ha)	Mean dbh ob (cm)	Stems/ha	Basal Area (m²ha)	Mean dbh ob (cm)
10·7				198	4·66	17·3
12·2	494	9·18	15·5			
13·7				198	8·56	23·4
15·2	494	17·08	21·1	198	12·23	28·2
18·3	494	24·94	25·4	198	19·70	35·6
21·3	489	32·71	29·2	198	27·13	41·9
24·4	484	40·36	32·5	198	34·55	47·2
27·4 Before Thinning						
27·4 Thinning	277	22·36	32·0			
27·4 Main Crop	198	25·23	40·4	198	41·99	52·1
30·5	198	31·45	45·0	198	49·40	56·4
33·5	198	37·70	49·3	198	56·84	60·5
36·6	195	43·55	51·1	195	63·73	64·5
39·6	193	49·33	57·2			
42·7	191	55·05	60·1			

TABLE 5.4

EXTRACTED VOLUMES (NET OF LOGGING WASTE) AT ROTATION AGE (m³/ha)

| | Yield Thinning Regime | | Direct Regime | |
	Volume	Mean dbh ob (cm)	Volume	Mean dbh ob (cm)
Thinning	147	32·0	–	–
Clearfelling	660	60·0	577	61·7
Total	807		577	
Mean Annual Increment	22·4 m³/ha/annum		22·2 m³/ha/annum	

In terms of total volume yield there is a negligible difference between the two regimes, but in terms of wood quality the direct regime is far superior. (See Table 5.5).

TABLE 5.5

MEAN ANNUAL INCREMENTS BY END USE CATEGORIES (m³/ ha per year)

	Yield Thinning Regime	Direct Regime
A. SAWN TIMBER		
Clears and superior grades	2·6	6·1
Other grades	4·5	4·1
Total sawn timber	7·1	10·2
B. PULPWOOD		
From sawmill slabs	3·0	4·3
From logs	9·3*	3·2
Total pulpwood	12·3	7·5
C. LOSSES IN SAWMILLING PROCESS	3·0	4·5
TOTAL	22·4	22·2

*Includes all logs extracted in the thinning; these are not suitable for sawing.

Under New Zealand conditions "yield thinning" does not increase total volume yields but it does result in poorer quality wood than is possible if the thinning (without yield) is done early to ensure that growth can be concentrated on the final crop trees only.

Stability is difficult to quantify but under New Zealand conditions trees become increasingly susceptible to windthrow after height 15–20 m, particularly if exposure is then increased by thinning. Yield thinning at height 27 m incurs this risk and many stands have suffered serious wind losses. On the other hand, ". . . since stand stability is undoubtedly increased by heavy early thinning . . .", (Chandler, 1970) the direct regime is less likely to suffer loss.

b. *Damage to Soil and Trees*
Removal of thinnings involves considerable soil disturbance and this must involve some root damage to residual trees, especially those along extraction tracks and near loading areas. As yet the effect of this damage on growth has not been assessed. Root infection is not usually a problem in New Zealand.

Damage to the tree stem in extraction thinning has been assessed – butt damage (the loss of some

bark from the lower portion of the tree) has been observed in every thinned stand – up to 25% of the remaining trees can be damaged in this way (Fenton *et al.*, 1965; Park, 1972).

Far more serious, though, than actual damage is the loss of potential final crop trees from major extraction roads and the loading areas. Management claims that this loss can be reduced to 3% but aerial photographs of the best thinned stands have shown area losses of 7% (J. B. Crowe, pers. comm.). Since these areas remain non-productive for the remainder of the rotation, this loss is serious. (The yield estimates for the yield thinning regime are therefore probably overestimates, since only a 3% area loss has been allowed for).

c. *Costs and Revenue*
The economics of the two regimes (and many others) have been intensively researched (Fenton, 1972a and b) and summarised (Fenton, 1972c). The relative profitability and break-even growing costs for the two regimes are given in Table 5.6.

In the calculations the thinnings are assumed to have made a net profit of $1 per m³ – in practice the operation would probably have made a loss.

TABLE 5.6
RELATIVE PROFITABILITY (INCLUDING SOCIAL COSTS) (1968 COSTS AND PRICES)

Criterion	Thinning Regime	Direct Regime
Land Expectation Value per ha ($NZ)*		
at 7% compound interest	—14	+240
at 10% compound interest	—65	+14
Internal Rate of Return	6·66	10·5
Break-even growing cost ($ per m³)		
7%	7·33	3·92
10%	19·08	7·55

*Excludes the price of land. $NZ 1·00=£0·56 approximately.
The direct regime is far more profitable than the yield thinning regime.
The real cost of yield thinning is the delay in the growth of the final crop trees.

Discussion

In discussing the results of his economic comparisons Fenton (1972c) concluded that the regime with a thinning yield was ". . . inferior in every respect to the direct regime; it costs more than twice as much per (m³), produced lower grades, needs as much labour, has greater managerial, physical, fire and marketing risks . . . Results are so different that no such production thinning should be prescribed; it has no advantage to compensate for its disadvantages".

The new direct regime has one additional major attraction. Soon after it was first proposed it became obvious that the very open stand conditions created by the heavy early thinning and pruning favoured the development of understorey weeds, grass, etc.

It was logical that this growth could be used for grazing (Knowles *et al.*, 1973) and research on this is now well beyond the experimental stage.

The concept of combined forestry and farming has won wide acceptance in New Zealand. When implemented it eliminates the one objection most theoreticians have to the direct regime: viz, that we are not fully utilising the site. With grazing the direct regime can claim to utilise the site fully and can produce intermediate yields of high quality, viz, animal products, which can be walked off the forest – this is in contrast to a thinning yield of poor quality wood that can only be removed at considerable expense and with at least some damage to the remaining stand, and can only be grown on regimes which are economically inferior.

REFERENCES

CHANDLER, K. C. (1970). Site Limitations on Pruning and Thinning. *New Zealand Forest Service, Forest Research Institute Symposium* 12(2): 85–88.

FENTON, R. T. (1972a). Economics of Radiata pine for Sawlog Production. *New Zealand Journal of Forestry Science* 2(3): 313–47.

FENTON, R. T. (1972b). Economics of Sawlog Silviculture which includes Production Thinning. *New Zealand Journal of Forestry Science* 2(3): 348–68.

FENTON, R. T. (1972c). Implications of Radiata pine Afforestation Studies. *New Zealand Journal of Forestry Science* 2(3): 378–88.

FENTON, R. T., JAMES, R. N., KNOWLES, R. L. and SUTTON, W. R. J. (1972). *Growth, Silviculture and the Implications of Two Tending Regimes for Radiata pine.* Proceedings Seventh Geography Conference, New Zealand. New Zealand Forest Service Reprint No. 635.

FENTON, R. T., MACKINTOSH, J. D. and HOSKINS, M. R. (1965). *Assessment Results from Production Thinnings of Young Stands of Radiata pine and Douglas fir.* New Zealand Forest Service, Forest Research Institute Silviculture Report No. 40 (unpublished).

FENTON, R. T., and SUTTON, W. R. J. (1968). Silvicultural Proposals for Radiata pine on High Quality Sites. *New Zealand Journal of Forestry* 13(2): 220–8.

KNOWLES, R. L., KLOMP, B. K., and GILLINGHAM, A. (1973). Trees and Grass – An Opportunity for the Hill Country Farmer. *Proceedings of the Ruakura Farmers' Conference* 1973. 110–21.

PARK, J. C. (1972). Assessments of Production Thinned Stands – *Pinus radiata. New Zealand Forest Service, Forest Research Institute, Economics of Silviculture Report* No. 52 (unpublished).

PENISTAN, M. J. (1960). Thinning Practice. *Forestry* 33(2): 149–73.

SHELBOURNE, C. J. A. (1970). Genetic Improvement in Different Tree Characters of Radiata pine and the consequences for Silviculture and Utilisation. *New Zealand Forest Service, Forest Research Institute Symposium* 12(2), 44–58.

SPURR, S. H. (1962). Growth and Mortality of a 1925 Planting of *Pinus radiata* on Pumice. *New Zealand Journal of Forestry* 8(4): 560–9.

SUTTON, W. R. J., and CROWE, J. B. (1972). Pruning of Radiata pine Dominants. Part 4. Effect of Pruning on Dominance, Growth and Stem Characteristics. *New Zealand Forest Service, Forest Research Institute Economics of Silviculture Report* No. 53 (unpublished).

SUTTON, W. R. J., and HARRIS, J. MADDERN. (1974). Effect of Heavy Thinning on Wood Density in Radiata pine. *New Zealand Journal of Forestry Science* 4(1): 112–5.

URE, J. (1949). The Natural Regeneration of *Pinus radiata* on Kaingaroa Forest. *New Zealand Journal of Forestry* 6(1), 30–38.

DISCUSSION

Van Laar: In South Africa there are serious doubts about the economics of so called high-pruning. Do you feel that there is any value in pruning to a height greater than 13 feet (approximately 4·0 m)?

Sutton: In what I have called the Yield Thinning regime, with relatively long rotations, I would not recommend pruning to the second log. With the Direct regime which involves a short rotation and where the effect of compound interest on costs is less, pruning of the second log is really worthwhile.

Whether or not one should prune the second log depends on the size of tree one is aiming at and the rotation length.

Busby: What do you mean by 'social costs' in Table 5.6?

Sutton: The social costs cover things like housing, septic tanks, cookhouses etc for employees. That is they are direct social costs incurred by the employees in the forestry department.

Paper 6

THINNING RESEARCH IN SOUTH AFRICA

By A. VAN LAAR

Faculty of Forestry, University of Stellenbosch

INTRODUCTION

In South Africa, afforestation with exotic tree species began around the turn of this century. *Pinus radiata*, *P. elliottii* and *P. taeda* were imported from U.S.A., *P. patula* from Mexico, *P. caribaea* from the Caribbean, *P. canariensis* from the Canaries, *P. pinaster* from Southern Europe, *Eucalyptus* and *Acacia* species from Australia. During the initial stage of forestry, the emphasis was on experiments to select species for specific climatic zones. Thereafter the emphasis shifted towards silvicultural operations such as pruning and thinning. During the early days of forestry, prior to 1935, thinnings were light and concurred with contemporary thinning practices in Europe. Economic conditions and the market situation in South Africa between 1930 and 1940 necessitated a drastic revision of the thinning regime. Planting espacement was increased from $1 \cdot 60 \times 1 \cdot 60$ to $2 \cdot 70 \times 2 \cdot 70$ m and rules, which were subsequently also adopted by private growers, were laid down to regulate stand density in state-owned plantations on sites of different qualities. After some minor changes, introduced in 1948, the recommended stem numbers per hectare, of the remaining stand, in plantations of fast-growing pines, such as *P. radiata*, *P. patula*, *P. elliottii* and *P. taeda* were as shown in Table 6.1.

These thinning prescriptions served as a guide in forest management, with the understanding that

TABLE 6.1

STEM NUMBER OF REMAINING STAND

Site quality I		Site quality II		Site quality III	
Age	Stems per hectare	Age	Stems per hectare	Age	Stems per hectare
0	1310	0	1310	0	1310
10	820	6	520	6	740
15	540	18	370	14	370
20	370	23	300	20	250
25	300	40	0	50	0
30	0				

they should be adapted to local conditions. During this period a regime of heavy early thinnings was economically justified because a market for small-sized timber e.g. for pulpwood, was virtually non-existent and the steep price-size gradient, which existed between 1930 and 1940, rendered heavy thinnings more profitable. The above thinning regime was based on Craib's growth studies in pine plantations (Craib 1939, 1947). Craib assumed that total volume production per hectare might be depressed as a result of heavy thinnings, but there was meagre statistical evidence with regard to the magnitude of the rate of depression. Market conditions and economic considerations however were of overriding importance.

THINNING RESEARCH

Since 1935 three directions in thinning research have been pursued.

1. Correlated Curve Trend projects
2. The application of growth models to mensurational studies in temporary sample plots
3. Replicated thinning experiments

1. Correlated Curve Trend Projects

C.C.T. experiments, devised by O'Connor (1935), are spacing trials, established with the ultimate goal of constructing sets of real growth series, for sites of different qualities. A single replicate contains 8 one-fifth acre plots with stem number varying between 125 and 3000 per hectare. As the establishment of sample plots with this range of stem numbers was impractical, all plots of a series were planted at $1 \cdot 80 \times 1 \cdot 80$ m (3000 stems per hectare) and progressively thinned, prior to the onset of competition. To this end, plot 1, selected at random from the group of 8 plots, was left unthinned and plots 2 and 8 were thinned during the second year after planting, the stem number being reduced from 3000 to 1500 stems per hectare. Plots 3 to 8 were thinned from 1500 to 1000 stems per hectare, as soon as the diameter growth of plot 1 dropped 0·05 inches below that of plot 2. Plots 4 to 8 were thinned from 1000 to 750 stems per hectare as soon as the diameter increment of plot 2 was below plot 3 etc. After the last thinning, which was carried out at the age of 9 to 10 years, the series contained plots with nominal densities of 125, 250, 375, 500, 750, 1000, 1500 and 3000 stems per hectare. Because of mortality, the actual stocking at 30 years however was below nominal stocking. The rate of mortality was dependent on stand density and was invariably highest in plots 1 and 2 with nominal densities of 3000 and 1500 stems per hectare respectively.

Preliminary results of C.C.T. experiments were published by Marsh (1957) and Pienaar (1965). Pienaar's studies are of particular interest. They deal with the application of the Chapman-Richard growth model to test the hypothesis that live basal area per hectare reaches an asymptotic level which – within a certain range of stand densities – is independent of stocking density. This asymptotic yield level is therefore a site parameter and expresses the capability of a site to support a certain live basal area. Pienaar's studies were based on mensurational records in the C.C.T. experiment at Mac-Mac in the Transvaal. The following conclusions were drawn:

1. The hypothesis of a common asymptotic live basal area yield for stand densities between 750 and 3000 could not be rejected.

2. The age of culmination of the rate of basal area growth was related to stand density. In plots with 3000 stems per hectare it culminated at 4 years, in plots with 500 stems per hectare at 7 years and in plots with 125 stems per hectare at 13 years.

3. The rate of basal area growth at culmination was directly related to stems per hectare. It was 2·20 m² per hectare for N=3000, 0·72 m² per hectare for N=500 and 0·30 m² per hectare for N=125.

4. After culmination, the rate of basal area growth in plots with high stand densities declined faster than in plots with wider spacings. The rate of basal area growth in plots with N=3000 dropped below the growth in plots with N=1500 at 9·8 years, below those with N=500 at 15 years and below plots with N=125 at 25 years.

5. At 14 years the mean true form factor in plots with N=3000 was 0·565, in those with N=500 it was 0·524 and in plots with N=125 the form factor was 0·495.

A more recent study (Reinstorf 1970) indicated that growth curves for live basal area in plots at Mac-Mac, with stand densities of 750, 1000, 1500 and 3000 per hectare converged at the age of 29 years. There were indications however that live basal area at the age of convergence did not represent an asymptotic value. Due to the excessively high mortality rate on plots, with a nominal stem number of 3000, basal area growth drops, after the age of 29 years, below that observed in plots with N=1500. This raises the question as to whether mortality must be explained in terms of the inability of a site to support live basal area beyond a certain level, or whether other factors are operative, in addition to competition. In plots with 3000 stems per hectare, the root system might, at older ages, be inadequate to meet the demand for water, thereby making the stand more vulnerable to drought conditions, prevailing in certain years.

Reinstorf's studies were carried out in *P. elliottii*, in C.C.T. experiments at Mac-Mac, Kwa-Mbonambi and Border. Similarly to Mac-Mac, the plot data for Kwa-Mbonambi indicated a tendency for a convergence of basal area growth curves, but the point of convergence had not yet been reached at the age of 31 years. The mensurational records of the Border-experiment however did not indicate the occurrence of an asymptotic live basal area. Apparently, site factors are of decisive importance and influence the observed growth patterns.

Each C.C.T. experiment includes 8 sample plots which are thinned at different ages and represent different degrees of thinning; these thinnings are carried out after competition has commenced, with the purpose of predicting the growth rate of thinned stands. Pienaar formulated the hypothesis that the growth rate of thinned stands is equal to that of those unthinned stands which have the same density as the former after thinning. In the unthinned stand this specific density will have been reached at an earlier age. Statistical tests were carried out by Pienaar (1965) in *Pinus elliottii* and by Joubert (1964) in *Pinus patula*. The growth rate of thinned plots was compared with that of unthinned plots of similar density but of different age, the observations being conceived as a random sample from a population of growth differences with a mean equal to zero. The tests confirmed Marsh's earlier postulation that the above growth hypothesis for thinned stands holds true for a wide range of stand densities. Undoubtedly the sample size, i.e. the number of thinned plots, available in each experiment was insufficient to conduct a high-powered statistical test and thus to detect small differences between the observed and hypothetical growth rate. This however does not impair the usefulness and scientific value of C.C.T.-

projects which constitute an imaginative approach in thinning research.

2. The Use of Response Equations

Multiple regression equations relating stand density and other stand characteristics to growth, were used by Grut (1970) and Crowe (1965). Grut's studies were based on mensurational records in permanent sample plots in *P. radiata*, the observations at different ages being interpreted as independent estimates of growth. A prediction equation was developed and tested for significance, including log stem number, age², height/age, height × stem number as explanatory variables and basal area increment as dependent variable. Crowe's studies were based on temporary plots in stands of *P. patula* of different ages and stand densities. They were measured once only and estimates for basal area growth were derived from increment cores. The regression equation included reciprocal values of age and stand density/age as explanatory variables to estimate basal area growth.

3. Replicated Thinning Experiments
3.1 Thinning Research in Poplars

Prior to 1965 the silviculture of poplar plantations followed the general pattern in South African man-made forests (Tingle 1966). *Populus deltoides* was generally planted at an espacement of $2 \cdot 70 \times 2 \cdot 70$ m. The severity of thinning varied slightly according to site quality. Site class I stands, with a mean height of approximately 31 m at the age of 20 years, were thinned at 4, 7, 10 and 12 years, site class II stands, with a mean height of 25 m at 20 years at 5, 8, 11 and 13 years. The trees of the first thinning, with a mean diameter of 13 to 14 cm, had no commercial value. In South Africa, *Populus deltoides*, is planted for matchwood, with a diameter o.b. at the thin end of the log of 15 cm and over. Theoretically, the first thinning could be utilised for chipboard and wood-wool, for which timber between 8 and 15 cm diameter is used, but in practice it is not utilised. The pre-1965 thinning regime, when expressed in stems per hectare are S% of the remaining stand, the latter defined as

$$\frac{100 \times \text{mean height,}}{\sqrt{\text{stems per hectare}}}$$ is given in Table 6.2.

In 1965 two replicated thinning experiments (Redclyffe) were established in site quality I stands, 8 and 9 years old respectively (Van Laar 1970). The S% after thinning was introduced as criterion for stand

TABLE 6.2
STEMS PER HECTARE AND S% IN POPULUS DELTOIDES

	Site quality I			Site quality II	
Age	N/hectare	S%	Age	N/hectare	S%
4	890	35·0	5	890	37·0
7	590	25·0	8	590	28·0
10	440	22·0	11	440	26·0
12	360	22·0	13	320	26·5

density and severity of thinning. Three severities of thinning were tested in an unrestricted random lay-out with 4 replications. In experiment I, S% index-values of 21, 27 and 32 and in experiment II index-values of 26, 29 and 34 were tested. In the analysis of variance, S% and error were identifiable sources of variation. A subsequent regression analysis, however, indicated that basal area level during the growth period was more suitable to predict the rate of volume growth. It reduced the standard error of the estimated growth rate significantly. Basal area level and S% of the remaining stand are obviously interrelated but the relationship is of a stochastic nature, primarily because S% as an

index of stand density does not account for differences between diameter distributions. If S% is replaced by basal area, the factor level does not represent a discrete variable. In consequence the effect of thinning can not be assessed by a normal analysis of variance. For this reason a regression analysis was carried out with basal area level instead of S% as explanatory variable to assess the effect of stand density on growth.

The relationship between periodic current volume and basal area level, during a response period of 6 years, shown in Fig 6.1, was:

Experiment I: $= Y - 39 \cdot 266 + 61 \cdot 0504 \log x \dots (1)$
Experiment II: $= Y - 4 \cdot 7389 + 27 \cdot 9248 \log x \dots (2)$

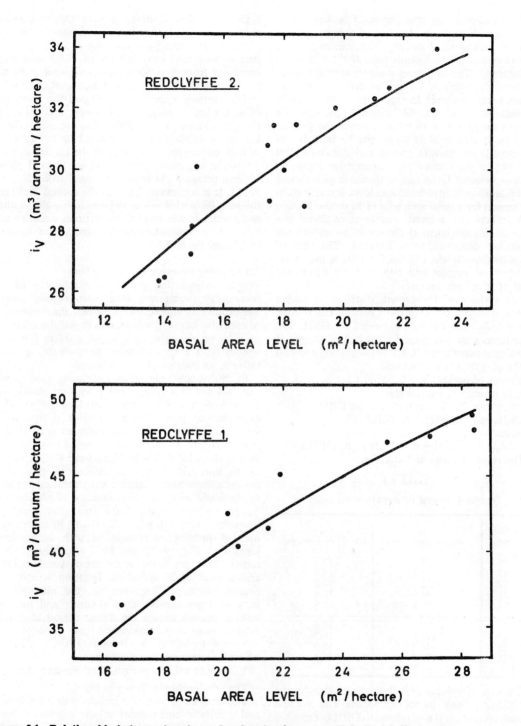

Figure 6.1 Relationship between basal area level and volume growth in Redclyffe 2 and 1.

The statistical analysis revealed a significant, curvilinear increase in the rate of volume growth with increasing stand density. The standard errors of the regression coefficients were 0·971 and 0·890 respectively. This indicates a significant difference between the rates of volume growth per unit increase basal area level. In experiment I, the periodic current increment was 34·2 m³/hectare/annum for a basal area level of 16 m² per hectare and 47·1 m³ for a basal area level of 26 m² per hectare. In experiment II the relevant growth estimates were 28·9 and 34·8 m² per hectare per annum respectively.

In experiment I, the rate of diameter growth was curvilinearly related to basal area level. It was 2·68 cm per annum for a basal area level of 16 m² per hectare and 1·57 cm for a basal area level of 26 m² per hectare. In experiment II there was no statistically significant departure from linearity. The rate of diameter growth was 1·98 cm for a basal area level of 16 m² per hectare and 1·15 cm for a basal area level of 26 m² per hectare.

For a study of the growth distribution within stands, during a 5-year growth period, the volume of the individual tree was regressed on DBH. The regressions were calculated for the lightest degree of thinning in experiment II, for the beginning and end of the growth period separately.

Beginning of period: $V_1 = b_o(DBH_1)^{b_1}$

End of period: $V_1 = c_o(DBH_2)^{c_1}$

Furthermore DBH_2 was regressed on DBH_1:

$$DBH_2 = a_o + a_1DBH_1 + a_2DBH_1^2$$

Hence:

$$i_v = c_o(a_o + a_1DBH_1 + a_2DBH_1^2)^{c_1} - b_o(DBH_1)^{b_1}.(3)$$

The result is given in Table 6.3.

TABLE 6.3

VOLUME GROWTH IN RELATION TO DBH

DBH_1 (cm)	i_v (dm³/annum/tree)	i_v (in % of average)
15	35.5	19.1
17	43.1	17.9
19	52.7	17.2
21	64.6	16.8
23	79.4	16.6
25	97.5	16.6
27	119.5	16.7
29	146.2	17.0
31	178.0	17.3

The rate of volume growth increases steeply and curvilinearly with increasing DBH. The volume growth percentage is also related to DBH but reaches a minimum for DBH=24 cm.

The relationship between value increment per unit area and basal area level reveals a trend, which is similar to that of volume growth. Due to a lower value of standing timber in the more heavily thinned plots, the indicating per cent, for a 5-year growth period, was negatively related to basal area and decreased from 20% for a basal area level of 20 m² per hectare to 18% for a basal area level of 25 m².

The thinning experiments revealed the necessity of a revision of planting espacement and thinning (Tingle and van Laar 1970). Planting espacement has been increased from 2·70×2·70 to 4×4 m. A first, commercial thinning will be carried out at 7 years in site class I and at 8 in site class II plantations, bringing the remaining stand to an S% of 32–33. It is recommended that the second and last thinning be carried out at 10 years in site class I and at 13 years in site class II plantations, again to an S% index of approximately 32% and a stem number of 220 per hectare.

3.2 Thinning Research in *Pinus radiata*

When sawtimber is grown in plantations of *P. radiata*, *P. patula* and other fast-growing pines, live-pruning is imperative to prevent the formation of excessive knots. Many studies reveal the effect of pruning on diameter and height growth, but few studies have been conducted to evaluate, quantitatively, its interaction with thinning.

In 1963 a combined thinning-pruning experiment was laid out in a 10-year old *P. radiata* plantation in the S.W. Cape Province (Van Laar 1973). The experimental plan was a split-plot design with stand density applied at three factor levels to whole-plots and severity of pruning assigned to sub-plots, also at three factor levels. There were 4 replications in an unrestricted random lay-out of treatment combinations. Stand density was expressed by S% of the stand after thinning, severity of pruning by % branch-free length of the tree after pruning. Stand densities with S%=30, 40 and 50 and severities of pruning corresponding with branch-free lengths of 50%, 65% and 80% respectively were tested. This produced 9 treatment combinations and a total of 36 sub-plots. Ignoring severity of pruning as a predictor-variable, the relationship between stem number after thinning and rate of volume growth during the 8-year period after the establishment of the experiment was:

$$Y = 8·411 + 0·05997 X - 0·0000333 X^2 \ldots \ldots (4)$$

where X = stem number per hectare

Y = rate of volume growth in m³ per annum

The relationship is shown in Fig 6.2.

The analysis of variance indicated that the linear and quadratic components of the regression sum of squares were highly significant.

The influence of both thinning and pruning on growth was re-assessed by a regression analysis

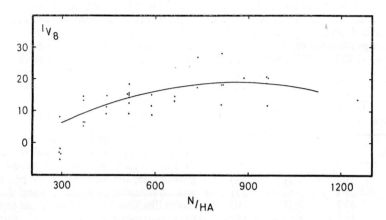

Figure 6.2 Relationship between stems per hectare and rate of volume growth.

with basal area level (X_1), severity of pruning (X_2), X_1^2, X_2^2, X_1X_2, $X_1^2X_2$, $X_1X_2^2$ and $X_1^2X_2^2$ as predictor-variables. It disclosed the existence of a curvilinear increase of basal area growth with increasing basal area level, a curvilinear decrease of basal area growth with increasing severity of pruning and significant interactions pruning x thinning. Similar results were obtained for volume growth. The relevant regression equations for volume growth were:

First year after pruning and thinning:

$$Y = 7.3170 + 0.1190\ X_1^2 - 1.2753\ X_2 - 0.00334\ X_1^2X_2 \quad \ldots \ldots \ldots \ldots \ldots \ldots \quad (5)$$

Seven-year period thereafter:

$$Y = 1.313 + 1.2753\ X_1 - 0.00232\ X_1^2X_2^2 \ \ldots \ (6)$$

with X_1 = average basal area during growth period

X_2 = severity of pruning

Y = rate of volume of growth in m³/hectare/annum

There was no statistical evidence of a relationship between stand density and rate of height growth or taper, but the rate of height growth during the 7-year response period was severely depressed by pruning, whereas the stems showed a tendency towards a cylindrical form.

In 1964 a thinning experiment was established in a 10-year old, site quality I stand of *Pinus radiata* on the slopes of Table Mountain. In each of three replicates one plot was left unthinned, a second and third plot were thinned. The mean S% after thinning, in this case defined as the mean distance between the trees expressed as a percentage of the regression height of the 20% thickest trees, was:

A-degree: S% = 18.2
B-degree: S% = 23.5
C-degree: S% = 31.5

The following rates of volume growth have been recorded:

Series	Degree	Volume growth in m³/hectare/annum		
		1964–1968	1968–1970	1970–1974
5	A	28.9	32.3	26.0
	B	32.5	30.1	28.7
	C	17.0	20.6	27.4
6	A	35.2	23.9	31.1
	B	36.5	28.7	28.3
	C	25.7	26.3	24.9
7	A	41.5	33.0	19.4
	B	45.3	35.1	38.8
	C	28.9	23.7	26.4

A statistical analysis disclosed highly significant differences between severities of thinning. Differences associated with blocks, periods and the interaction periods x thinning were non-significant. The average periodic current volume increment during the 10-year period 1964–1974 was:

A-degree: i_v = 30.3 m³/hectare/annum
B-degree: i_v = 34.3 m³/hectare/annum
C-degree: i_v = 24.7 m³/hectare/annum

The experimental data indicate, but do not present convincing statistical evidence, that the rate of volume growth of unthinned stands is below that of stands exposed to the B-degree of thinning.

The diameter distribution was studied by fitting the beta-distribution:

$$f(x) = c\ (x-a)^\alpha \cdot (b-x)^\gamma \ \ldots \ldots \ldots \ldots \quad (7)$$

to the plot data in 1964, 1968, 1970, 1971 and 1974 of series 5. Table 6.4 gives the characteristics of the distributions. (See also Fig. 6.3).

Volume growth of the individual tree, between

1964 and 1974 was regressed on DBH_{1964}. In series 5 the relationship was curvilinear in the A-plot and linear in the B- and C-plots (see Fig. 6.4). The relevant regression equations were:

A-degree: $\log Y = -2\cdot832 + 2\cdot79277 \log X \ldots$ (8)
B-degree: $\quad Y = -5\cdot941 + 0\cdot70755 X \ldots\ldots$ (9)
C-degree: $\quad Y = -3\cdot672 + 0\cdot56680 X \ldots\ldots$ (10)

TABLE 6.4

VALUE OF a, b, α AND γ

	a	b	α	γ
		A-degree		
1964	7·5	20·5	1·93	2·57
1968	7·5	27·5	2·39	2·21
1970	7·5	30·5	3·43	6·03
1971	7·5	32·5	3·43	6·03
1974	7·5	35·5	3·11	5·55
		B-degree		
1964	11·5	21·5	2·08	2·84
1968	16·5	28·5	1·62	1·26
1970	17·5	31·5	1·48	0·82
1971	18·5	33·5	1·40	0·70
1974	20·5	36·5	1·21	0·64
		C-degree		
1964	10·5	20·5	1·42	1·69
1968	15·5	27·5	0·66	0·74
1970	16·5	31·5	0·99	0·79
1971	19·5	33·5	0·66	0·69
1974	20·5	37·5	1·28	0·99

The differences between slopes and intercepts of B- and C-plots were non-significant. For the same initial DBH however, the growth rate in the B- and C-plots was significantly greater than that observed in A-plots. The periodic current volume growth of the individual tree was also expressed as a % of the stem volume at the midpoint of the 10-year growth period and subsequently regressed on DBH in 1964. The regression was non-significant in 5 plots, in 2 plots it was significant with a positive and in 3 plots significant with a negative value of the regression coefficient.

The relationship between crown size, degree of thinning and growth rate of individual trees as well as the relationship between needle-biomass and growth rate, and the effect of competition on growth was investigated in series 5, 6 and 7 at Tokai. The crown diameter, crown length and tree height of all trees were measured as well as the distance between the study trees and 7, 8 or 9 adjacent ones. Multi-phase sampling was used to estimate the needle-biomass of 12 trees, distributed over thinning treatments A, B and C.

Crown diameter and crown length decreased linearly with increasing stand density. The relevant equations were:

mean crown width (m) $= 4\cdot1919 - 0\cdot0017$ (stems per hectare) $\ldots\ldots\ldots\ldots\ldots\ldots$ (11)
mean crown length (m) $= 21\cdot410 - 0\cdot0081$ (stems per hectare) $\ldots\ldots\ldots\ldots\ldots\ldots$ (12)

The $\dfrac{\text{crown length}}{\text{crown width}}$ ratio was also related to stand density. It had a value of 5.12 for 200 stems per hectare and 5.45 for 1400 stems per hectare.

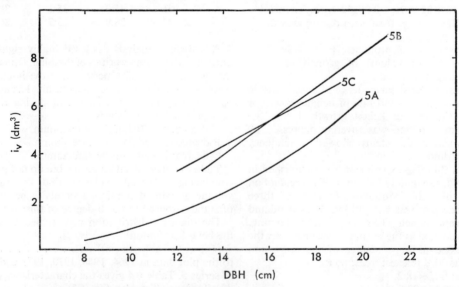

Figure 6.4 Relationship between breast height diameter (DBH) and rate of volume growth of single trees. i_v (dm³) = volume increment in cubic decimetres.

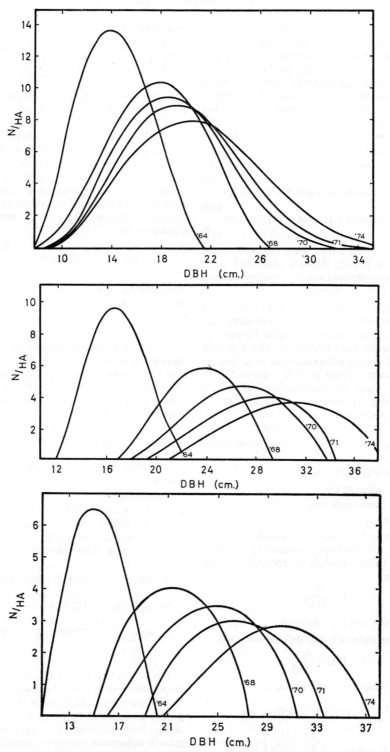

Figure 6.3 Beta-function fitted to diameter distributions of A (top), B (centre) and C (bottom) degrees of thinning.

For each tree in all A-, B- and C-plots the volume growth over the 7-year period 1964–1971 was determined and subsequently related to the area of the horizontal crown projection in 1971. The relationship could be satisfactorily expressed by a second-degree equation. An analysis of covariance did not disclose heterogeneity amongst slopes, but growth-means, adjusted to a common value of the area crown projection, differed highly significantly. The relevant equations were:

A-degree: $Y = 72 \cdot 07 + 44 \cdot 6808\ X - 1 \cdot 2496\ X^2$
$$\dots\dots\dots\dots\dots\dots (13)$$
B-degree: $Y = 113 \cdot 30 + 44 \cdot 6808\ X - 1 \cdot 2496\ X^2$
$$\dots\dots\dots\dots\dots\dots (14)$$
C-degree: $Y = 169 \cdot 57 + 44 \cdot 6808\ X - 1 \cdot 2496\ X^2$
$$\dots\dots\dots\dots\dots\dots (15)$$

For trees of a given crown area, the growth rate of single trees in heavily thinned stands is greater than that in lightly thinned stands, possibly because of reduced root competition.

Needle-biomass studies revealed the effect of stand density on certain relationships. For secondary branches of a given diameter, needle biomass in C-plots was greater than in A-plots. For a branch diameter of $0 \cdot 5$ cm the difference was 16%. The relationship between volume growth – derived from stem analyses – and needle-biomass disclosed the effect of thinning on growth rate per unit needle weight. In the A-, B- and C-plots it was $2 \cdot 70$, $2 \cdot 92$ and $3 \cdot 16$ dm^3 per kg needles respectively.

In order to assess the effect of competition within stands, the trees surrounding a study tree were arranged according to the ratio:

$$Q = \frac{\text{DBH of adjacent tree}}{\text{distance from study tree}}$$

from small to large values of Q. The 1-tree sample plot, i.e. the plot with $n = 1$, contained the tree with the largest value of Q, the study tree itself not being included. It represents a basal area per hectare:

$$BA_1 = \frac{d_1^2}{4D_1^2}$$

where $d_1 = $ DBH, and $D_1 = $ distance. The competition index CI, was defined as

$$CI_1 = BA_1 = \frac{d_1^2}{4D_1^2}$$

For $n = 2$, the basal area per hectare is

$$BA_2 = \frac{d_1^2 + d_2^2}{4D_2^2}$$ and CI_2 is defined as:

$$CI_2 = \frac{BA_1 + BA_2}{2} = \frac{d_1^2 \left(1 + \dfrac{D_2^2}{D_1^2}\right) + d_2^2}{8D_2^2}$$

In general: $CI_n =$

$$\frac{d_1^2 \left(\dfrac{D_n^2}{D_1^2} + \dfrac{D_n^2}{D_2^2} + \dots 1\right) + d_2^2 \left(\dfrac{D_n^2}{D_2^2} + \dfrac{D_n^2}{D_3^2} + \dots 1\right) + d_n^2}{4nD_n^2}$$

In the A-plots, CI_n was calculated for $n = 1 \dots 9$, in the B-plots for $n = 1 \dots 8$ and in the C-plots for $n = 1 \dots 7$. These indices were subsequently related to volume growth, tree height being introduced as a second explanatory variable, but primarily serving as a concomitant variable. The sum of squares, associated with the partial regression of volume growth on CI was expressed as a percentage of the total sum of squares of dependent variable, but after fitting tree height. The relevant regression sum of squares were:

$n =$	1	2	3	4	5	6	7	8	9
	SS regression in % of total, after fitting tree height								
A-degree	9·4	9·8	10·8	13·3	14·3	15·6	16·9	18·4	19·8
B-degree	6·4	12·0	12·8	12·5	11·0	9·6	10·0	10·0	–
C-degree	5·1	6·1	5·1	5·0	3·9	3·2	3·2	–	–

In the A-plots the regression sum of squares increases from $n = 1$ to $n = 9$. This seems to indicate that the first adjacent 9 trees compete with a study tree, but it remains undisclosed whether the 9th tree makes a significant contribution towards this regression. In the B-plots, the regression sum of squares decreases beyond $n = 3$ and in the C-plots beyond $n = 2$. A general trend is also apparent that CI_n contributes less to the regression of growth on competition index, as stands are more heavily thinned.

An analysis of covariance with volume growth as dependent variable, CI_4 and tree height as explanatory variables did not disclose heterogeneity amongst slopes, but highly significant differences amongst levels. The relevant regression equations are:

A-degree: $i_v = -309 \cdot 23 + 26 \cdot 128\ (H) - 2 \cdot 575\ (CI_4)$
$$\dots\dots\dots\dots\dots\dots (16)$$
B-degree: $i_v = -182 \cdot 724 + 26 \cdot 128\ (H) - 2 \cdot 575\ (CI_4)$
$$\dots\dots\dots\dots\dots\dots (17)$$
C-degree: $i_v = -73 \cdot 012 + 26 \cdot 128\ (H) - 2 \cdot 575\ (CI_4)$
$$\dots\dots\dots\dots\dots\dots (18)$$

For a given value of CI_4 and for a given tree height, the rate of volume growth in heavily thinned sample plots exceeds those in more lightly thinned plots significantly. This indicates that the index of competition satisfactorily explains the observed growth differentiation within stands, associated with competition, but does not account for all factors which define competition.

LITERATURE

CRAIB, I. J. (1939). Thinning, pruning and management studies on the main exotic conifers in South Africa. *Dep. of Agr. and For., Bull.* 196.

CRAIB, I. J. (1947). The silviculture of exotic conifers in South Africa. *Fifth Brit. Emp. For. Conf.*, London 1947.

CROWE, N. B. (1965). Growth, yield and economics of *Pinus patula* in the Natal Midlands. *D.Sc. thesis*, Stellenbosch.

GRUT, M. (1970). *Pinus radiata; Growth and Economics.* Cape Town 1970.

JOUBERT, A. F. (1964). An analysis of the relative profitability of various thinning degrees in stands of *Pinus patula* in the Eastern Transvaal. *M.Sc. thesis.* Stellenbosch.

MARSH, E. K. (1957). Some preliminary results from O'Connors Correlated Curve Trend (C.C.T.) experiments on thinning and pruning and their practical significance. *Comm. For. Conf. Austr. and N. Zealand* 1957.

PIENAAR, L. V. (1965). Quantitative Theory on Forest Growth. *Thesis, University of Washington.*

REINSTORF, L. O. (1970). The influence of Stand Density on Growth of *Pinus elliottii. M.Sc. thesis*, Stellenbosch.

TINGLE, A. C. (1966). Silviculture, volume and yield of *Populus deltoides. Ann. of Univ. of Stell.* Vol. 41, Series A, No. 10.

TINGLE, A. C. and VAN LAAR, A. (1972). The Economics of Thinnings in Poplar Plantations *Comm. No.* 31/1972, *Faculty of Forestry*, Stellenbosch.

TINGLE, A. C. and VAN LAAR, A. (1970). The Silviculture of *Populus deltoides* in South Africa.

VAN LAAR, A. (1970). Vorlaufige Ergebnisse eines Pappel- Durchforstungs-Versuches in Sudafrika. *Forstw. Centrallblatt* 89:141–152.

VAN LAAR, A. (1973). Needle-biomass, Growth and Growth Distribution of *Pinus radiata* in South Africa in Relation to Pruning and Thinning. *Forschungsbericht* No. 9/1973, *Forstl. Forschungsant.* Munchen.

Paper 7

GROWING SPACE MEASUREMENTS—COMPLEMENTARY TO THINNING EXPERIMENTS

By AXEL MARTIN JENSEN

Royal Veterinary and Agricultural University Copenhagen, Denmark

1. Introduction

The present study tests a single tree/distance dependent growth model, following the terminology of Munro (1973) – as a means of predicting growth of forest stands subjected to different treatments of thinning.

Although it is generally held that single tree modelling owes its existence to the development of computers, it is worth mentioning that Rewentlow (1816) drew very sound conclusions concerning the management of beech and oak forests in Denmark on the basis of stand mapping and single tree volume growth measurements. However, computerized modelling does not yet seem to have produced results of immediate practical application. The present study is unfortunately not an exception in this respect.

Despite these limitations, distance dependent single tree modelling ought to continue because the approach is logical. The present paper tries to throw light on some of the reasons for the shortcomings.

2. Working Hypothesis

Loetsch (1953) and Prodan (1965) demonstrate that the volume increment of a single tree is closely related to its diameter as a pure matter of mathematics and general increment laws.

Strand (1959) finds the standard deviation of the regression of volume increment on basal area of

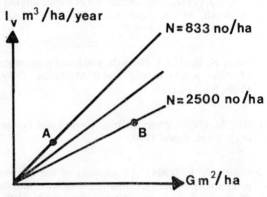

Figure 7.2

single trees in uneven aged stands of Norway spruce in Norway to vary between 12 and 50%. Personally I have found this standard deviation for even aged stands of Norway spruce in Denmark to vary between 10 and 30%.

The question to be considered here is whether or not some of the residual variations can be explained by differences in competition. For instance, can the larger volume increment of tree A in Figure 7.1 be attributed to a larger growing space than the growing space of tree B, so that generally speaking there exists a function of the type:

$$i_v = b_0 + b_1 g + b_2 a \dots \dots \dots \dots \dots (1)$$

where i_v = volume increment of single tree
g = basal area of single tree
a = growing space of single tree
b_{0-2} = regression coefficients

If this is the case a transformation effected by dividing the growing space into the function will produce the following relationship between stand parameters:

$$I_v = b_0 + b_1 G + b_2 N \dots \dots \dots \dots \dots (2)$$

where I_v = volume increment in m³/ha/year
G = basal area in m²/ha
N = number of stems in no/ha

Here tree A will represent a lower stem number than tree B, see Figure 7.2.

This working hypothesis is in accordance with the conclusions of Løvengreen (1951).

3. Lay-out and Measurements

The investigation was undertaken in a 76 years old

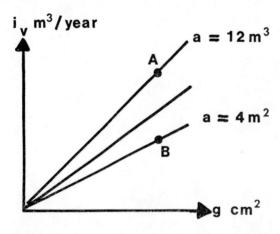

Figure 7.1

even-aged stand of Norway spruce, situated on a similar locality 1·5 km away from the thinning experiment in Gludsted Plantation, described by Bryndum (1969). The stand had the following parameters:

Age	76 years
Stem number, N	1200 no/ha
Height, H_g^-	15·4 m
Diameter, D^-	17·7 cm
Basal area, G^-	29·3 m²/ha
Stem volume, V	248 m³/ha
Site class	5·3 CMM

It corresponds well with the thinning grades B in the thinning experiment, but has a slightly better site class. However, a comparison of the results from the single tree measurements with the sample plot data from the thinning experiment should be possible.

The area chosen was divided into 10 equal parts of 100 trees each. In each part a permanent sample plot was established, which was measured for the first time in the autumn of 1967 and for the second time in the autumn of 1973.

The following measurements were undertaken on each plot:

	1967	1973
—$d_{1·3}$ with precision tape, one measuring mark. Error 0·2%, Jensen (1967)	X	X
—$d_{1·3}$ on 25 sample trees with precision tape, but with two measuring marks. Error 0·12 mm, Jensen (1967)		
—h on the 25 sample trees with JAL. Error about 1%	X	X
—$d_{o·1h}$ on the 25 sample trees with precision tape.	X	X
—$f_{o·1h}$ the true stem wood form factor, by felling 6 of the 25 sample trees		X
—x- and y-coordinates of the 25 sample trees and their neighbours		X

The volume increment of the sample trees was calculated making the following assumptions:
1. That $f_{o·1h}$ within each plot did not vary with the stem dimensions, Prodan (1965).
2. That $i_{fo·1h}$ the increment in true form factor, in a mature stand of Norway spruce is insignificant and can be put equal to zero, Jensen (1971).

4. The Growing Space Measurement
The model used in this investigation is similar to that of Jack (1967) and Schulz (1968) and takes, as in the model of Schulz, the diameter of the tree and its neighbours into account. Only in the present programme the growing space has been calculated assuming competition proportional to different powers of the diameters in the following manner:

$$e_i = l_i \left(\frac{d_s^c}{d_s^c + d_i^c} \right) \quad \dots \dots \dots \dots (3)$$

l_i = distance of i'th neighbour

e_i = distance of bisector on the joining line from the sample tree to the i'th neighbour

d_s = diameter of sample tree

d_i = diameter of i'th neighbour

See Figure 7.4.

The growing space has been calculated under the following hypothesis:

$$c = 0·0, 0·5, 1·0, 1·5 \dots \dots \dots \dots \dots 5·0$$

In Figure 7.3 and 7.4 the growing space is demonstrated for 3 test trees with competition respectively $c = 0·0$ and $c = 2·0$. Under the last assumption it will be seen on Figure 7.4 that tree B and C exert competition on A even if they are not immediate neighbours. By raising the power in the competition equation (3) the whole neighbourhood of the sample tree is taken into account, and not only the surrounding trees.

The growing space giving the biggest reduction in mean square in the equation (1) is defined as the best measure.

5. Results
The function used in the regression analyses is the simple linear model, equation (1), logarithmic transformation gave in all cases bigger mean squares.

For the material as a whole, significant influence of the growing space was found only when using the competition factor $c = 5·0$:

$i_v = b_o + b_1 g$	s = 24·6%
$i_v = b_o + b_1 g + b_2 a$	s = 24·4%

Even if the influence of the growing space is significant, $F_{1/244} = 4·48$, one must admit that it is of no importance as a means of predicting tree growth besides the diameter.

The growing space, taking the diameters of the neighbouring trees into account, embraces a small bias. The figures for the material as a whole are as follows:

c=	0·0	1·0	1·5	2·0	2·5
Bias %	+0·0	+2·6	+3·4	+3·9	+4·0

c=	3·0	3·5	4·0	4·5	5·0
Bias %	+3·8	+3·0	+1·9	+0·6	—0·6

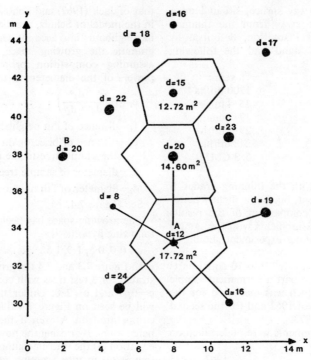

Figure 7.3   Growing space with equal competition between neighbours.

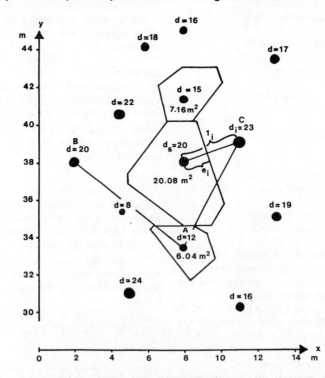

Figure 7.4   Growing space with competition proportional with the square of the diameter.

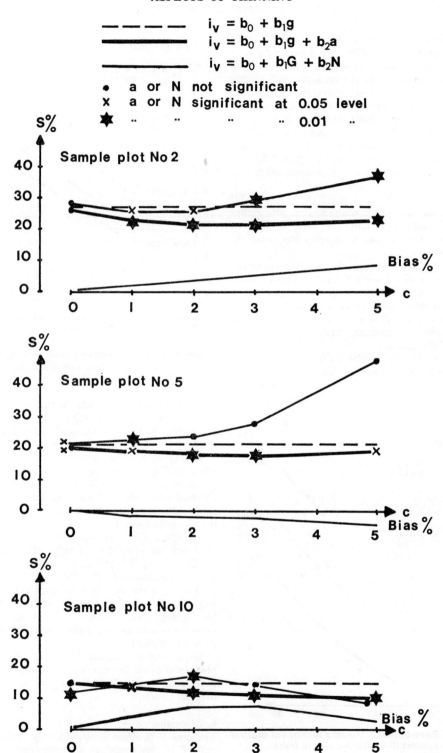

Figure 7.5   Standard deviation, significance and bias in relation to power of competition for 25 single trees on 3 selective sample plots.

In respect of bias it seems that the growing space measures can be used to reflect stand parameters.

Analysis of variance shows, however, that the material is heterogeneous. Accordingly each sample plot has been considered separately. Regression analysis of each sample plot reveals a significant correlation with the growing space in 3 sample plots whereas in the 7 others the growing space does not seem to have any influence. The results for the three significant plots are represented in Figure 7.5.

If the data are divided by the growing space and equation (2):

$$I_v = b_o + b_1 G + n_2 N \dots \dots \dots \dots \dots (2)$$

is used in the regression analysis, one gets rather confusing results especially for high powers of competition. This means of analysis has therefore been abandoned.

Figure 7.6 shows the fit of the function (1) to the data of sample plot 2 using the competition factor: $c = 2$. In Figure 7.7 this regression equation is transformed into stand parameters by dividing by the growing space, demonstrating the relationship between volume increment, basal area and stem number of the stand.

In Figure 7.8 the results from the single tree measurements are compared with the increment figures from the thinning experiment described by Bryndum (1969), by entering the sample plot basal

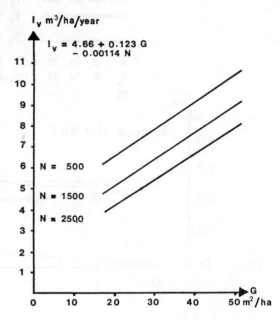

Figure 7.7 The regression equation from Figure 7.6 converted into stand parameters.

areas and stem numbers from the thinning experiment in the regression equations from the three significant sample plots, and consequently calculating the mean for each thinning grade.

Taking into consideration that it is a mature stand of Norway spruce, and that the single tree measurements refer to a stage 10 years older, the correspondence between the thinning experiment and the results from the 75 single tree measurements is quite impressive.

In Figure 7.9 a possible use of the single-tree approach to spacing is finally demonstrated. In the D_3 grade a D-B thinning is simulated by leaving the plots untouched from 1951 and onwards. It is thus the stem number in 1951 and the basal area in 1951 plus 20 years' increment which is entered into the regression equations. It appears that this treatment 20 years later gives the highest current increment of all plots.

Single tree measurements may in this way complete established thinning experiments by indicating a possible result of treatment not included in the original lay-out.

6. Discussion

The crucial problem is that in only 3 sample plots out of 10 the measures of inter-tree competition contribute significantly to a better prediction of tree growth than the mere use of tree diameters. This is

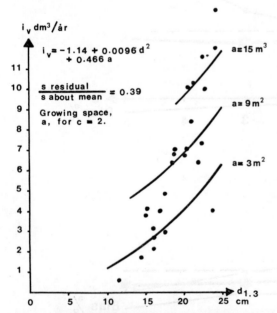

Figure 7.6 Sample plot 2. Volume increment plotted against diameter for single trees. ivdmar/ar = annual volume increment in cubic decimetres. d1.3 = diameter in centimetres, measured at breast height.

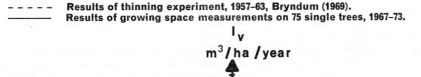

Results of thinning experiment, 1957–63, Bryndum (1969).
Results of growing space measurements on 75 single trees, 1967–73.

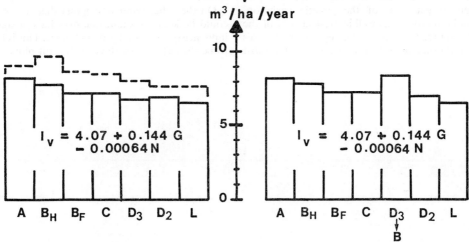

I_v
m^3 / ha / year

$$I_v = 4.07 + 0.144\,G - 0.00064\,N$$

$$I_v = 4.07 + 0.144\,G - 0.00064\,N$$

A B_H B_F C D_3 D_2 L

A B_H B_F C D_3 D_2 L
↓
B

Figure 7.8: Single tree measurements for all three significant plots, 75 trees in all, compared with sample plots results from thinning experiment.

Figure 7.9: Single tree measurements for all three significant plots only simulating a D-B thinning initiated on the D_3 plots in 1951.

not exceptional in competition studies, Adlard (1973). The following discussion aims at clarifying some of the reasons.

Stem rot
About half of the trees are attacked by stem rot in varying degree. An analysis of the 60 trees felled for the form factor measurements revealed no correlation between the degree of attack and the volume increment. This is in accordance with the findings of Henriksen (1952).

Errors of measurements
There are two possibilities:
a. *The growing space measurement used is inadequate as a measure of competition.*
Newnham (1972) discusses different growing space measurements and suggests that in a humid fertile region it is the crown competition which is important, competition is consequently only exerted by the immediate neighbours, whereas in dry regions with poor soils it is a question of root competition, where an individual tree can have up to 30 competitors. The growing space model used makes room for both situations. The better performance of growing space with high competition power of c, see Figure 7.5, indicates that the latter is the case on the locality in question. In accordance with the results of Hamilton (1969) it is believed that refinement of the growing space model is not the most important problem.

b. *The volume increment of the individual tree is*

determined with an error, which overshadows the effect of the growing space.
As pointed out by Mitchell (1972) the relation between growing space and the individual tree is a matter of physiology. Therefore stem volume increment might be an inadequate measure, dry matter production would be better, bio-mass the best. With this reservation the error of measurement of the volume increment of the individual tree will be subjected to an estimation.

A regression analysis on the whole material:
$$i_v = b_0 + b_1 i_g$$
reveals that the basal area increment counts for $86\cdot4\%$ of the variation in volume increment among individual trees. Errors in the other components can therefore be more or less disregarded and approximately assessed to 50%.

The volume increment is determined in two ways, one on the basis of the $d_{1\cdot3}$ measurements, the other one on the basis of the $d_{0\cdot1h}$

A regression analysis of:
$$i_{v0\cdot h1} = b_0 + b_1 i_{v1\cdot3}$$
gives a standard deviation of $14\cdot5\%$. As this standard deviation is composed of the error on both estimates, the error of $i_{v1\cdot3}$ which is used in the analysis may have the following proportion:
$$\sqrt{10^2 + (0\cdot136 \times 50)^2} = 12\%$$
Therefore a defective measurement of the volume increment of the individual tree is probably not the reason for lack of significance.

Variation in Site Factors and Genetic Variation.
The very reason for introducing the basal area as first variable in the stepwise regression analyses has been to get hold of the genetic variation, variation in micro site as well as past history of the tree in the stand. The result of the regression analyses may indicate that these factors are by far the most important in determining the current volume increment of a single tree rather than the actual growing space.

On the other hand it suggests that if site factors could be kept constant, one may have a significant influence of the actual growing space. This is believed to be the case on the three significant plots.

REFERENCES

ADLARD, P. G. (1973). *Development of an empirical competition model for individual trees within a stand.* IUFRO, Proceedings of Meetings 1973, Working Party S4.01–4. Department of Forest Yield Research, Research Notes nr. 30. 1974. Royal College of Forestry. Stockholm. Pg. 22–37.

BRYNDUM, H. (1969). A thinning experiment in Norway Spruce in Gludsted Plantation. *Det Forstl. Forsøgsv. Danm.* Bd. XXXII, hf. 1. København, pg. 5–187.

HAMILTON, G. J. (1969). The Dependence of Volume Increment of Individual Trees on Dominance, Crown Dimensions, and Competition. *Forestry,* Vol. 42, no. 2. Oxford, pg. 133–144.

HENRIKSEN, H. A. and JØRGENSEN, ERIK, (1954). Fomes annosus Attack In Relation To Grade Of Thinning. An Investigation On The Basis Of Experiments. *Det Forstl. Forsøgsv. Danmark,* Bd. XXI, pg. 215–252.

HENRIKSEN, H. A. (1958). The Increment and Health Condition of *Sitka Spruce* in Denmark. *Det Forstl. Forsøgsv. Danm.* Bd. XXIV, hf. 1. København, pg. 1–372.

JACK, W. H. (1967). *Single Tree Sampling In Even-Aged Plantations for Survey And Experimentation.* Papers XIV. IUFRO-KONGRESS, VI, section 25, München, pg. 379–403.

JENSEN, A. M. (1967). Eine Versuchsmessung mit Umfangmessband. *Dansk Skovforen. Tidsskr.* 52:167–188. København.

JENSEN, A. M. (1971). *Massetilvaekstmalingens metode og nøjagtighed belyst pa grundlag af stammean-alyser.* Royal Veterinary And Agricultural University. Department Of Forestry. Copenhagen. pg. 1–31.

LOETSCH, F. (1953). Massenzuwachsermittlung durch Bohrspanproben unter Anwendung Mathema-tisch-statisticher Methoden. *Zeitschrift F. Weltforstwirtschaft* 16–3.

LØVENGREEN, J. A. (1951). Thinning of beech in Denmark since 1900, illustrated statistically and assessed theoretically. *Det Forstl. Forsøgsv. Danm.* København, pg. 271–354.

MITCHELL, K. J. (1972). *Suppression And Death. Proceedings: Tree Growth Simulation Workshop. Forest Management Institute, Ottawa, Ontario.* Internal Report FMR-25 pg. 71–78.

NEWNHAM, R. M. (1972). *Stand Models – Where Do We Go From Here? Proceedings: Tree Growth Simulation Workshop. Forest Management Institute, Ottawa, Ontario.* Internal Report FMR-25, pg. 7–17.

REVENTLOW, C. D. F. (1816). *A Treatise on Forestry.* 3. ed. published by the society of Forest History, Hørsholm, Denmark, 1960. Pg. 1–142.

SCHULZ, B. (1968). Programm zur Berechnung des Standraumes in einschichtigen Beständen (APAC). *Allgem. Forst- u. Jagdz.* 139. Jahrg. Frankfurt am Main I. Pg. 232–234.

STRAND, L. (1959). The accuracy of some methods for estimating volume and increment on sample plots. *Det Norske Skogforsøksvesen* nr. 52. Norge, pg. 283–392.

PRODAN, M. (1965). *Holzmesslehre.* Sauerländers Verlag. Frankfurt a.M.

MUNRO, D. D. (1973). *Forest Growth Models – a Prognosis.* IUFRO, Proceedings of Meetings 1973, Working Party S4.01–4. Department of Forest Yield Research, Research Notes. Nr. 30, 1974. Royal College of Forestry. Stockholm. Pg. 7–21.

DISCUSSION

Bredberg: In equation (1) ($i_v = b_1g + b_2a$) the variable 'g' (basal area of a single tree) must be in turn the result of the growing space, variable 'a', available to the tree in the past. Researchers working in Sweden on models like this have found that if you omit 'g', which is highly correlated with 'a', you would find that the competition variable was much more significant.

Jensen: From the practical viewpoint, if 'g' is as significant as 'a', you don't need to consider 'a'. My point is that 'g' is very easy to determine, but

including 'a' adds to the overall significance.

Bredberg: In order to establish the effect of 'a', one must make radical changes in the growing space of individual trees by thinning. With light thinnings, as in this case, there is no such radical change.

Jensen: You are suggesting that I should have chosen a heavily thinned stand?

Bredberg: I suggest that both lightly and heavily thinned stands should have been used.

GENERAL DISCUSSION ON PAPERS 1-7 (FIRST SESSION)

Bredberg: Today we have had a lot of information about research into yield aspects, but my main interest is in the logging operation of thinning. We have heard of two alternatives, namely, selective thinning and geometric thinning. I think each of these is unrealistic. Selective thinning is not realistic because paths must be created for machine access. Geometric thinning is not very realistic for silvicultural reasons in many conditions. What is the proper compromise between selective and geometric thinnings? Experiments showing the difference between geometric and selective thinnings don't really tell you the proper combination of the two.

Hamilton: I think I would go along with much of that. I would say that by experimenting with extreme treatments of line thinning and selective thinning, you can expect to simulate the effects of combinations of these treatments. I do not think it is necessary to put down specific experiments of specific combinations of all these. For one thing you are highly unlikely to experiment with treatments that you would choose at the end of the day. You would be very lucky in fact if you did. By straddling various alternatives and simulating various combinations of these you can get results which are sufficiently accurate for our needs.

Bredberg: Can you really simulate a treatment involving removal of rows but selective thinning between rows?

Hamilton: Well, I am quite confident about doing this. Perhaps the answers will not be perfect but I think the results you get will be good enough for the kind of decisions you will have to make.

Kramer: While most of us are concerned with short periods in the lives of forests we should be careful to consider the whole rotation, which means that we may pass from a phase of geometric thinning to selective thinning. The losses we make in the first place will be for a short period of the rotation only. The whole rotation may give only a small loss or perhaps no loss at all. Secondly, we should be less concerned with the production of all trees but rather more concerned about the final crop trees and their production.

Rowan: I think the key word from the title of this Project Group is 'economics' because it is perfectly clear that it is the economics of a particular country that is going to determine what in fact happens. In those countries which are suffering severe fibre shortage I am quite sure we are going to need a rather different approach to yield studies. For example, most of the discussions today are centred on the stemwood but in may parts of the world we are looking at prospects of using branches, tops, needles and other parts of the tree besides the stem. So far this has not been a popular study with research people, not least because it is highly difficult to measure. Research along these lines probably has not been done because it was of very little practical value. I think this is no longer the case. We are already now wanting to know how much total fibre we can get and this is going to have an influence on our thinning regimes and other related topics such as the correct provenance of the various species. We have to get away from this fixation about the stem.

Young: I would like to disagree with you in that the total forest is not difficult to measure. I have been doing it for 15 years.

Fries: Perhaps by measuring branches, roots etc yield researchers will come to a better understanding of thinning because it is rather stupid to try to explain their biological process by measuring just one part of the plant.

W. Sutton: I cannot understand this obsession with total mass. The agriculturist isn't worried about the top of the carrot. He is only interested in the part that really matters, the root, and for us it is the main stem.

Rowan: With respect I disagree. He would certainly be interested in the tops if you could sell them and, in fact, he can sell them.

Fries: We have seen some figures today which show that systematic thinning like line thinning, instead of selective thinning, leads to a loss. But this is not a very great loss. Should we not move over to line thinning, bear this loss and harvest much more cheaply? I doubt it.

van Laar: If it means we cannot improve our seed by selective thinning then this would be a bad policy. If we adopt line thinning exclusively we will lose a number of the best trees.

Kramer: Systematic thinning is the solution we must choose because of the fact that stands were established much too densely and this is the only way to improve the stands. Perhaps in future we will not need to do this as we will have given the trees enough room from the start, and we could then go direct to selective thinning.

DER EINFLUSS VERSCHIEDENER DURCHFORSTUNGSARTEN AUF WACHSTUM UND BESTANDESSCHÄDEN UNTERSUCHUNGSERGEBNISSE AUS FICHTENBESTÄNDEN IN DER BUNDESREPUBLIK DEUTSCHLAND

Von H. KRAMER

1. Grundsätzliches

Als materielles Ziel der Fichtenwirtschaft (*Picea abies*) in Mitteleuropa wird heute i.a. der höchste Waldreinertrag angestrebt. Dieses Ziel beinhaltet eine gute Zuwachs- und Wertleistung, sowie eine hohe Resistenz des Bestandes gegen Schäden. Zu diesem Zweck sollen die Bestände relativ weitständig begründet (etwa 3000 Pflanzen je ha), in der Jugend stark und im späteren Alter nur noch schwach durchforstet werden.

Größere Probleme bestehen bei der Bestandespflege der früher eng begründeten (mit 4500 bis 10000 Pflanzen je ha) Fichtenjungbestände. Je dichter die Kultur gepflanzt war und je größer die standortsbedingten Gefahren, wie Schnee und Wind sind, um so früher muß aus waldbaulichen Gründen eine Stammzahlverminderung erfolgen. Aus wirtschaftlichen Gründen ist man bemüht, insbesondere diese ersten Stammzahlverminderungen durch Läuterung oder Durchforstung zu mechanisieren. Durch schematische Eingriffe, wie Reihen- und Gassenhieb, kann der Einsatz von Maschinen sehr gefördert werden.

In 12 bis 20-jährigen Fichtendickungen mit Bestandesmittelhöhen zwischen 2 und 6 m wurde die Stammzahl durch Entnahme jeder 2., 3. oder 4. Reihe reduziert. Diese frühzeitigen Eingriffe förderten den Zuwachs (9, 16) und insbesondere die Resistenz des Bestandes gegen Schnee- und Windschäden ganz erheblich.

Bei der ersten Durchforstung wird an Stelle der früher allgemein üblichen Niederdurchforstung eine *Auslese-*, eine *Reihen-* oder *Gassendurchforstung* bzw. Kombinationen dieser Durchforstungsarten verwendet. Bei der Auslesedurchforstung werden eine bestimmte Anzahl herrschender Bäume (300 bis 600 Bäume je ha) durch Entnahme anderer herrschender Bäume intensiv gefördert (1, 13, 16). Diese Durchforstungsart ist betriebswirtschaftlich und waldbaulich günstiger als die Niederdurchforstung. Eine stärkere Mechanisierung ist jedoch nur bei Reihendurchforstung (11) und Gassendurchforstung möglich (14). Die Reihendurchforstung, bei der wir i.a. jede 4. Reihe schlagen, eignet sich für die "Langholz-methode"; hierbei werden die Bäume in langer Form durch Pferd oder Seil gerückt. Bei der Gassendurchforstung werden mehrere nebeneinanderliegende Reihen oder schräg zur Pflanzrichtung laufende Streifen gehauen. Diese etwas breiteren Streifen dienen als Rücke- und Arbeitsgassen. Die Gassendurchforstung kann mit einer gleichzeitig durchgeführten individuellen Auslesedurchforstung kombiniert werden. Sie wird v.a. bei der "Kurzholz-methode" angewendet.

Diese sehr schematischen Eingriffe und hiermit verbundenen stark mechanisierten Durchforstungssysteme rufen viele biologische Probleme hervor. Im folgenden soll insbesondere auf den Einfluß verschiedener Durchforstungsmethoden auf den Massen- und Wertzuwachs sowie auf Bestandesschäden eingegangen werden.

2. Massen und Wertzuwachs

2.1 Allgemeines

Zur Prüfung des Massen- und Wertzuwachses bei verschiedenartiger Durchforstung wurden in Fichtenjungbeständen der Bundesrepublik Deutschland einige Versuche angelegt, bei denen schematische Eingriffe mit individueller Durchforstung verglichen wurden.

Bei der bisher üblichen Aufarbeitung mit Einmannmotorsägen haben Auslesedurchforstung und schematische Reihen- oder Gassenhieb viele betriebswirtschaftliche Vorteile gegenüber der Niederdurchforstung. Da bei den beiden erstgenannten Durchforstungen die Dimensionen deutlich stärker sind als bei der Niederdurchforstung, sind hier die Arbeitsleistung und der Verdienst der Waldarbeiter größer, die Werbungskosten geringer. Brutto- und Nettoerlös für das eingeschlagene Holz sind bei diesen Durchforstungsarten wesentlich höher als bei der Niederdurchforstung.

Bei der geometrischen Durchforstung (Reihen- und Gassenhieb) ist der Arbeitsfortschritt wegen geringerer Laufwege zusätzlich größer; außerdem sind hierbei Rückekosten und Verwaltungskosten niedriger als bei einer individuellen Durchforstung (17).

TABELLE 8.1

BETRIEBSWIRTSCHAFTLICHER VERGLEICH, FICHTENDURCHFORSTUNG HARDEGSEN, ABT. 51

ECONOMIC COMPARISON, NORWAY SPRUCE THINNING SAMPLE PLOTS, HARDEGSEN, DEP. 51

Df-Art Type of thinning	Anfall je ha Efm o.R. Yield from thinning per hectare m³ of timber u.b.	$\bar{V}$ Fm (%) $\bar{V}$ m³ (%)	Leistung je Std. Fm (%) Performance per hour m³ (%)	Verdienst je Std. DM (%) Earnings per hour DM (%)	Werbungskosten+Soz. Kost. je Fm DM (%) Felling costs and social costs per m³ DM (%)	Erlös je Fm DM (%) Revenue per m³ DM (%)	Netto-erlös (7-6) je Fm DM Net revenue (7-6) per m³ DM	Netto-erlös je ha DM Net rev. per hectare DM	Rücke- u. Erntetechnik Logging and harvesting technique	Verwaltungskosten Administration costs
(1)	(2)	(3)	(4)	(5)	(6)	(7)	(8)	(9)	(10)	(11)
Niederdfg. Low thinning	37	0,027 (100)	0,12 (100)	4,39 (100)	64,88 (100)	+35,15 (100)	−29,73	−1097	schlecht bad	hoch high
Auslesecfg. Crown thinning	54	0,078 (288)	0,23 (191)	5,10 (116)	39,00 (60)	+41,20 (117)	+2,20	+ 119	schlecht bad	hoch high
Reihendfg. Line thinning	52	0,064 (236)	0,23 (191)	5,35 (121)	41,94 (64)	+40,63 (115)	− 1,31	− 68	gut good	extrem niedrig very low

2.2 Hardegsen, Abt. 51 b

In einem seinerzeit 34-jährigen, im $1,25 \times 1,25$ m-Verband erwachsenen Fichtenbestand I/II Ertragsklasse (Ertragstafel Wiedemann, mäß. Durchforstung 1936/42=dGZ 11) wurden im März 1967 drei verschiedene Durchforstungsarten in dreifacher Wiederholung angelegt. Bei der Erstdurchforstung wurden 25% der Grundfläche entnommen als:

1. Niederdurchforstung
2. Auslesedurchforstung
3. Reihendurchforstung.

Tabelle 8.1 gibt einen betriebswirtschaftlichen Vergleich. Aus der Übersicht ist zu erkennen, daß die Niederdurchforstung besonders ungüstig abschneidet. Der Nettoerlös je ha betrug im Jahr 1967 minus 1100, — DM je ha, während bei den beiden anderen Durchforstungen die Werbungskosten durch den Erlös etwa gedeckt waren (13).

In Tabelle 8.2 wird der 5-jährige Volumenzuwachs der drei Durchforstungsarten verglichen (13).

Die Zuwachsanalyse macht deutlich, daß der

TABELLE 8.2

ZUWACHSVERGLEICH VON NIEDERDURCHFORSTUNG, AUSLESEDURCHFORSTUNG UND REIHENDURCHFORSTUNG
BEI FICHTE: HARDEGSEN ABT. 51 b   5-JÄHRIGER VOLUMENZUWACHS

5-YEAR VOLUME INCREMENT IN NORWAY SPRUCE AFTER DIFFERENT THINNING METHODS HARDEGSEN, DEP. 51 b

Durchforstungsart Type of thinning	Zuwachs je ha Vfm (%) Volume increment m³ per ha (%)	s	Zuwachsverlust je ha in Vfm (%) loss of increment m³ per ha (%)	bezogen auf 100 J. (%) in 100 years (%)	Zuwachs der 800 stärksten Bäume je ha Vfm (%) Increment of the 800 thickest trees per ha m³ (%)	s	Zuwachs der 400 stärksten Bäume je ha Vfm % Increment of the 400 thickest trees per ha m³ (%)	s
(1)	(2)		(3)	(4)	(5)		(6)	
Niederdfg. Low thinning	86,0 (100)	±5,0	–		57,8 (100)	±5,3	35,4 (100)	±3,9
Auslesedfg. Crown thinning	84,3 (98)	±5,0	1,7 (2)	0,1	62,9 (109)	±5,5	40,3 (114)	±4,0
Reihendfg. Line thinning	79,3 (92)	±5,1	6,7 (8)	0,6	57,0 (99)	±5,4	37,3 (105)	±3,9

TABELLE 8.3

ENTWICKLUNG DES KRONENPROZENTES DER 400 STÄRKSTEN BÄUME JE HA

DEVELOPMENT OF CROWN PERCENT OF THE 400 THICKEST TREES PER HECTARE

Durchforstungsart Type of thinning	III. 1967	XII. 1971
Undurchforstet Unthinned	53%	38%
Niederdurchforstung Low thinning	54%	48%
Auslesedurchforstung Crown thinning	53%	52%
Reihendurchforstung Line thinning	53%	48%

5-jährige Volumenzuwachs bei Niederdurchforstung und Auslesedurchforstung nahezu gleich hoch ist. Die Reihendurchforstung hat einen nicht gesicherten Zuwachsverlust von 8%; dieser Zuwachsverlust wirkt sich auf die gesamte Umtriebszeit von 100 Jahren nur mit 0,6% aus. Durch die Reihen- und besonders durch die Auslesedurchforstung wird der Zuwachs der stärksten Bäume mehr gefördert als durch eine Niederdurchforstung. Der Volumenzuwachs der 400 stärksten Bäume ist bei der Reihendurchforstung 5%, bei der Auslesedurchforstung 14% höher als bei der Niederdurchforstung.

Für den nachhaltigen Massen- und Wertzuwachs der Zukunftsbäme und für deren Resistenz gegen Schneebruch ist die Kronenausbildung von großer Bedeutung. In der Übersicht wird die Entwicklung der relativen Kronenlänge (Kronenlänge im Verhältnis zur Baumhöhe=Kronenprozent) der Versuchsflächen bei verschiedener Behandlung angegeben.

Aus der Übersicht ist zu erkennen, daß die 400 stärksten Bäume je ha bei der Versuchsanlage eine gute Kronenausbildung (Kronenprozent = 53) hatten. Innerhalb von nur 5 Jahren sank das Kronenprozent dieser Bäume bei den undurchforsteten Vergleichsflächen von 53 auf 38 %. Die individuelle Niederdurchforstung und die schematische Reihendurchforstung hatten den gleichen Effekt auf die Kronenentwicklung. Mit einem Kronenprozent von 48 konnte hierbei eine sehr gute Krone erhalten werden. Am wirkungsvollsten konnten die Kronen durch die Auslesedurchforstung gefördert werden (Kronenprozent = 52) (13).

Als Ergebnis dieser Versuchsflächen ist festzustellen: Die Auslesedurchforstung erlaubt die beste Zuwachspflege. Die Reihendurchforstung bietet die größten wirtschaftlichen und technischen Vorteile und gestattet eine durchaus befriedigende Bestandespflege.

2.3 Brilon, Abt. 131 a

In einem seinerzeit 45-jährigen, in $3,0 \times 1,0$ m Reihenverband begründeten Fichtenbestand I. Ertragsklasse (Ertragstafel Wiedemann, mäß. Durchforstung 1936/42 = dGZ 12) wurden im Herbst 1969 25 % des Vorrates einmal in individueller Niederdurchforstung, zum anderen durch Aushieb jeder 4. Reihe entnommem (15). Bei dem Reihenhieb entstanden somit 6 m breite Gassen. Die Behandlungsart wurde $2 \times$ wiederholt. In Tabelle 8.4 wird der 4-jährige Grundflächenzuwachs angegeben (15).

Der 4-jährige Grundflächenzuwachs liegt zwischen 8,9 m² und 11,1 m². Es ist kein eindeutiger Unterschied des Zuwachses beider Durchforstungsarten festzustellen. Im Durchschnitt liegt der 4-jährige Zuwachs bei der Reihendurchforstung 3 % niedriger.

Der Zuwachsverlust bei diesem extremen Eingriff ist erstaunlich gering. Er dürfte sich auf die 100-jährige Umtriebszeit nur unbedeutend auswirken.

Bei einer Kombination von geometrischen Eingriffen mit Auslesedurchforstung dürften kaum Zuwachsverluste auftreten.

2.4 Lautenthal, Abt. 158 b

Im Harzforstamt Lautenthal (11) wurde vor 45 Jahren in einem seinerzeit 55-jährigen Fichtenbestand II/III Ertragsklasse (Ertragstafel Wiedemann, mäß. Durchforstung 1936/42 = dGZ 9) 2/3 des Vorrates durch Aushieb jeder 2. und 3. Reihe entnommen. Der Bestand zeigt heute eine gute Massen- und Wertleistung. Da leider keine Versuchsfläche existiert, werden in Tabelle 8.5 die Aufnahmedaten der Weiserfläche mit den entsprechenden Daten der Wiedemann'schen Ertragstafel für mäßige und starke Durchforstung verglichen.

Obwohl ein Vergleich mit der Ertragstafel gerade hier sehr fragwürdig sein muß, ist doch aus der Tabelle zu erkennen, daß der Bestand trotz eines extremen geometrischen Eingriffs heute eine gute Massen- und Wertleistung hat. Bei einer Stammzahlhaltung, die zwischen der der mäßigen und der der starken Durchforstung liegt, hat er die gleiche Vorratshaltung wie die mäßige Durchforstung. Seine Dimensionen sind noch größer als bei der starken Durchforstung. Der Wert des Bestandes je ha – ausgedrückt in werbungskostenfreiem Erlös – ist

TABELLE 8.4

ZUWACHSVERGLEICH VON STARKER NIEDERDURCHFORSTUNG UND REIHENDURCHFORSTUNG BEI FICHTE BRILON, ABT. 131 a 4-JÄHRIGER GRUNDFLÄCHENZUWACHS

4-YEAR VOLUME INCREMENT AFTER LOW THINNING AND LINE THINNING IN A 45 YEAR OLD NORWAY SPRUCE STAND PLANTED 3×1 METRES

Flächen-Nr. Number of sample plot	Durchfor-stungsart Type of thinning	Grundfläche vor Durchforstung m² je ha Basal area before thinning m² per ha	4-j. Grundflächen-zuwachs je ha (1970–1973) m² 4 year basal area increment (1970–1973) m² per ha	Zuwachsprozent 1970–1973 % Percentage of basal area increment 1970–1973 %
I a	Reihendfg.	35,23	11,1	28,6
I b	Line thinning	37,26	8,9	23,7
I a+I b	Line thinning	36,25	9,5 (97 %)	26,1
II a	Niederdfg.	33,48	9,6	28,7
II b	Low thinning	35,82	10,0	27,7
II a+II b	Low thinning	34,65	9,8 (100 %)	28,3

TABELLE 8.5

VORRAT UND WERT EINES 100-JÄHRIGEN FICHTENBESTANDES NACH GASSENDURCHFORSTUNG VOR 45 JAHREN IM VERGLEICH MIT DER ERTRAGSTAFEL

STANDING CROP AND VALUE OF A 100-YEAR-OLD NORWAY SPRUCE STAND AFTER A VERY HEAVY STRIP-THINNING (2 OF EVERY 3 ROWS FELLED 45 YEARS AGO.) COMPARISON WITH YIELD-TABLE (WIEDEMANN) FOR MODERATE AND HEAVY LOW THINNING

Behandlung	Alter	EK1	Stamm-zahl je ha	h_m m	d_m cm	g/ha m²	V/ha Vfm m.R. Derbh.	V/ha Vfm m.R. 10 cm Zopf	V/ha Vfm m.R. 15 cm Zopf	V/ha Vfm m.R. 20 cm Zopf	werbungskosten-freier Erlös DM je EFm	DM je ha
Treatment	Age	Yield class	Number of trees per ha	mean height m	mean Diam. cm	Basal area per ha m²	Volume to 7 cm per ha m³	Volume to 10 cm per ha m³	Volume to 15 cm per ha m³	Volume to 20 cm per ha m³	Ner revenue per m³ DM	DM
(1)	(2)	(3)	(4)	(5)	(6)	(7)	(8)	(9)	(10)	(11)	(12)	(13)
Gassendfg. Strip thinning	100	II,4	420	27,4	36,0 (100%)	42,7	564 (100%)	561 (100%)	547 (100%)	508 (100%)	69 (100%)	33·079 (100%)
E.T. m.Df. Yield table mod. low thinning	100	II,4	601	27,6	30,0 (83%)	41,4	553 (98%)	548 (98%)	517 (95%)	431 (85%)	57 (83%)	26·793 (81%)
E.T. st.Df. Yield table heavy low thinning	100	II,6	381	27,6	33,8 (94%)	33,5	447 (79%)	443 (79%)	429 (78%)	373 (73%)	65 (94%)	24·697 (75%)

daher ganz besonders hoch. Trotz des sehr starken Eingriffs im Alter von 55 Jahren entsprachen Aststärken, Jahrringbildung und Ausformung der Fichten weitgehend denen eines angrenzenden Bestandes, der individuell durchforstet worden war (11).

3. Schäden an Boden und Bäumen

3.1 Allgemeines

Die besonders in Schweden (2) beobachteten starken Zuwachsverluste infolge von Gassenhieben sind fast ausschließlich durch die verwendete Technik bei der Holzernte und beim Holzrücken verursacht. Boden- und Wurzelschäden sind nach Fries (7, 8) bei Raupenfahrzeugen geringer als bei Radfahrzeugen und können bei Abdecken der Gassen mit Reisig ganz vermieden werden. Aufbauend auf die schwedischen Untersuchungen wurden einige geometrische Verfahren der Stammzahlverminderung geprüft.

3.2 Maschinelle Streifenläuterung

Im Forstamt Hardegsen, Solling (danach auch in anderen Forstämtern Süd-Niedersachsens und Nord-Hessens) wurde zur streifenweisen Stammzahlreduzierung in extrem dichten Fichtenjungbeständen eine Spezialraupe eingesetzt. Die Bestände hatten eine Mittelhöhe von 8,5 m, einen mittleren Brusthöhendurchmesser von 9 cm und einen maximalen Brusthöhendurchmesser von 23 cm. Verwendet wurde eine 75 PS Hanomag Raupe K 7 B mit V-förmigen Planierschild und einem Gleichrichter. Das Schild war nach dem Schneepflugprinzip konstruiert und besitzt an der Unterseite ein waagerecht laufendes Schneidmesser. Im Abstand von ca. 8 m wurden mit diesem Gerät auf 2,50 m breiten Streifen Bäume bis zu 23 cm Brusthöhendurchmesser abgeschnitten und umgedrückt. Die Stundenleistung dieser Streifenläuterung betrug 1/2 ha. Die Kosten je ha (einschließlich der Kosten für zwei weitere Waldarbeiter für Hilfsarbeiten) betrugen 120, – – bis 160, – – DM je ha (10).

Boden- und Wurzelschäden wurden durch diesen Einsatz ganz vermieden, da die Raupe über den Teppich der abgeschnittenen Bäume fuhr. Eine unbedeutende Anzahl der stehenden Randbäume wurde verletzt. Diese Bäume wurden von den begleitenden Waldarbeitern mit der Motorsäge abgeschnitten, so daß keine beschädigten Bäume im Bestand stehenblieben. Der Käferbefall an dem liegenden, nicht aufgearbeiteten Material war unbedeutend. Eine Bekämpfung der Käfer war nicht erforderlich. 4 Jahre nach der Maßnahme ist das Kronendach über den Streifen weitgehend geschlossen. Die gut bekronten Bäume haben die erheblichen Schnee- und Windschäden der letzten Jahre sehr gut überstanden.

3.3 Gassendurchforstung in Kurzholzmethode

Bei einer Gassendurchforstung in einem 35-jährigen Fichtenbestand I. Ertragsklasse aus Pflanzung im 1,5 × 1,5 m-Verband in Hardegsen wurden 3 verschiedene Verfahren geprüft.

Block I. Entnahme jeder 9. und 10. Reihe. Auslesedurchforstung im Zwischenstreifen. Gassenbreite 4,50 m.

Block II. Entnahme jeder 12. und 13. Reihe. Zu beiden Seiten der Gasse bei 4 Reihen Auslesedurchforstung, 3 Mittelreihen undurchforstet.

Block III. Entnahme jeder 4. und 5. Reihe. Keine Maßnahme im Zwischenstreifen.

Das Holz wurde in der Kurzholzmethode aufgearbeitet (2 m langes Schichtholz mit Rinde). Vorrücken mit Hand zur Gasse. Belassen der Äste und Kronenspitzen auf der Gasse. Rücken des Holzes auf Gassen mit Kurzholz-Rückezug B.M. Volvo SM 868.

Bei diesen Verfahren traten keine Boden- oder Wurzelschäden auf.

Die Leistung und die verursachten Stammschäden sind aus Tabelle 8.6 zu entnehmen.

Aus der Übersicht ist zu ersehen, daß die reine Gassendurchforstung im Block III die größte Leistung und damit den höchsten Verdienst für die Waldarbeiter ermöglicht. Dieses Verfahren wäre auch für eine weitere Technisierung durch Erntemaschinen am geeignetsten. Auf der anderen Seite sind gegen dieses Verfahren erheblich biologische bestimmte Bedenken vorzubringen. Während im Block I und II nur 4% bzw. 3% der Zukunftsbäume stark beschädigt wurden, wurden hierbei 9% der zur Ästung ausgewählten Endstämme schwer verletzt (14).

3.4 Verwendung der Baumholzerntemethode in Fichtenjungbeständen

Im Münchener Institut für Holzkunde und Forstnutzung (21, 22) wurden zur Erstdurchforstung in Fichtenbeständen verschiedene Methoden der Langholzaufarbeitung geprüft. Die Durchforstung wurde nach rein waldbaulichen Gründen durchgeführt. Je ha wurden zwischen 700 und 2300 Bäume, bzw. zwischen 15 und 42 Festmeter entnommen. Hierbei wurden die Bäume unentastet auf Rückegassen und fischgrätenangeordneten Seillinien mit Schlepper gerückt. Die Arbeit wurde zu verschiedenen Jahreszeiten durchgeführt. Die hierbei insbesondere am Stammfuß auftretenden Rindenschäden waren bedenklich hoch. Beim Rücken während des Winters wiesen 4% bis 14% der vorherrschenden und herrschenden Bäume mittlere und große Schäden auf. Im Sommer wurden sogar 17% bis 20% dieser Bäume stärker beschädigt. Aus biologischen Gründen

TABELL 8.6

VERGLEICH VERSCHIEDENER GASSENDURCHFORSTUNGEN

COMPARISON BETWEEN VARIOUS METHODS OF STRIP THINNING

*stacked cubic metre

Block Nr. Behandlungsart / Number of sample plot Type of thinning	Hiebsanfall je ha Efm o.R. (% d. Vorrats) / Yield from thinning per ha m³ of timber harvested u.b. (%)	Leistung je Std. Rm / Performance per hour st. c. m.*	Verdienst je Std. DM / Earnings per hour DM	Werbungs kosten je Rm DM / Felling costs and social costs per st. c. m. DM	Rückekosten je Rm DM / Bringing costs per st. c. m. DM	Anzahl d. Z-Bäume je ha / Number of elite trees for pruning per ha	Beschädigte Z-Bäume je ha absol. (in %) / Number of damaged elite trees per ha (%)	Beschädigte Z-Bäume je 100 lfd. m Gasse / per 100 m strip length
I. Gassendurchforstung 10,5 m Zwischenstreifen mit A.Df. / I. Cutting of every 9th and 10th row. Between the cutting-strips crown thinning	92,8 (~40%)	0,58	7,91	14,30	7,60	327	13 (4%)	2,0
II. Gassendurchforst. 15 m Zwischenstreifen mit teilw. A.Df. / II. Cutting of every 12th and 13th row. Crown thinning in the 4 rows on each side of the strips. No thinning in 3 remaining rows	79,8 (~35%)	0,58	7,91	14,30	7,60	305	8 2,6%	1,6
III. Gassendfg. 3 m Zwischenstreifen ohne Dfg. / III. Cutting of every 4th and 5th row. No thinning in the remaining 3 rows	92,0 (~40%)	0,66	9,00	14,30	7,60	300	27 (9%)	2,0

sollten diese Ganz-Baummethoden nur während des Winters angewendet werden.

In Hardegsen verwendeten wir die Langholz-Erntemethode bei der Reihendurchforstung. Im Gegensatz zu den Münchener Methoden wurde hierbei schematisch jede 4. Baumreihe geschlagen und auf der entstehenden Arbeitsgasse geastet. Äste, Kronen und schwache, nicht verwendbare Bäume blieben auf der Gasse liegen. Das Holz wurde anschließend mit Pferd über den entstandenen Reisigteppich gerückt. Irgendwelche nennenswerten Boden- oder Rindenschäden konnten bei diesem Verfahren nicht beobachtet werden (16).

4. Wind- und Schneebruchschäden

4.1 Windschäden
In der Jugend und somit zur Zeit der ersten Stammzahlreduzierung sind die Fichtenbestände noch weniger von Wind bedroht. Die Gefährdung durch den Wind steigt abhängig von der Baumhöhe deutlich mit zunehmendem Bestandesalter (5, 6, 18, 19). Zur Vermeidung von Windschäden sollten daher stärkere Durchforstungseingriffe nur in Jungbeständen durchgeführt werden; ältere Bestände sind dagegen möglichst geschlossen zu halten, um dadurch ein zu starkes Ausschwingen der Baumkronen zu vermeiden. Besonders wurfgefährdet sind die Fichten unmittelbar nach der Duchforstung, sowie auf flachgründigen und nassen Böden. Diese allgemein bekannten Gesetzmäßigkeiten traten auch bei der

Windwurfkatastrophe in Norddeutschland am 13.11. 1972 deutlich hervor. Unsere Fichtenjungbestände in Hardegsen haben auch nach Reihen- und Gassendurchforstung i.a. den Wind gut ausgehalten. Stärker geschädigt wurden lediglich die Bestände, die unmittelbar vor dem Sturm durchforstet waren. Ein Einfluß der Durchforstungsart war nicht festzustellen. In unseren 1972 durchforsteten Versuchsflächen war die starke Niederdurchforstung sogar erheblich stärker geschädigt als die Reihen- und die Auslesesdurchforstung.

4.2 Schneeschäden
Die Schneebruchschäden treten im Gegensatz zu den Windschäden vor allem in Jungbeständen auf. Die Bestände, die zur ersten Durchforstung anstehen, sind daher besonders schneebruchgefährdet. Unsere Untersuchungen im Solling (4, 15, 24) bestätigten bereits bekannte Untersuchungen (23). Lang bekronte und mehr abholzige Fichten sind besonders schneebruchresistent. Das Ausfallprozent infolge Schneebruch steigt proportional mit dem mittleren Schlankheitsgrad und sinkt mit dem Kronenprozent (s. Abb. 8.1 und 8.2). Innerhalb eines Bestandes nimmt das Ausfallprozent mit zunehmendem Durchmesser ab (Abb. 8.3).

Eine Minderung der Bestandessicherheit gegen Schnee wird allgemein als Folge schematischer geometrischer Eingriffe befürchtet. Die Erfahrungen der Praxis über Schneebruch nach Reihen- und Gassen-

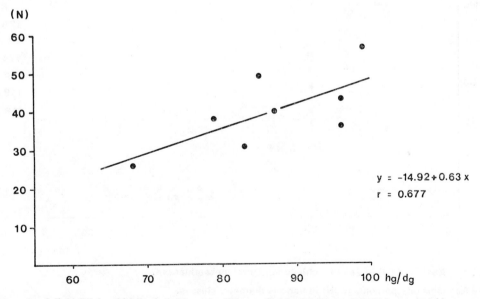

Abb. 8.1   Ausfall % **(N)** im Abhängigkeit vom mittleren Schlankheitsgrad (h$_g$/d$_g$).

Figure 8.1   Mortality percentage **(N)** as related to mean taper (h$_g$/d$_g$).

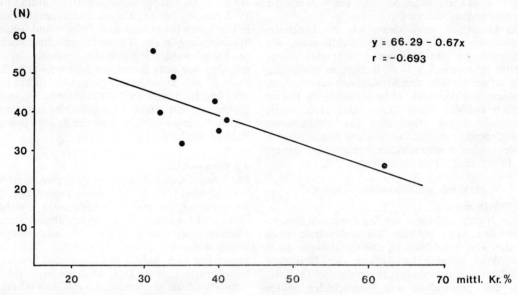

Abb. 8.2   Ausfall % (N) im Abhängigkeit vom mittleren Kronen %

Figure 8.2   Mortality percentage (N) as related to mean crown per cent

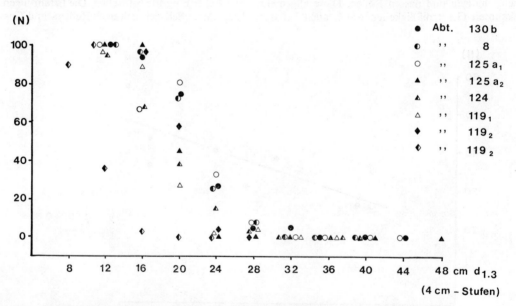

Abb. 8.3   Ausfall % (N) in den verschiedenen Durchmesserklassen.

Figure 8.3   Mortality percentage (N) in various diameter classes.
           Abteilung = compartment.
           4cm Stufen = 4 cm steps.
           d 1·3 = breast height diameter.

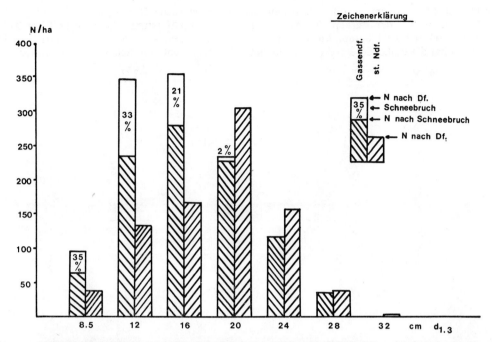

N/ha

Zeichenerklärung

Abb. 8.4 **Stadtforstamt Brilon, Abt. 131. Stammzahlverteilung bei Starkeklassen nach Gassendurchforstung und Schneebruchschaden im Vergleich zur starken Niederdurchforstung.**
Schneebruchschaden entstand nach der Gass endurchforstung fast ausschliesslich in den schwachen Bäumen der Stärkeklassen 8-16 cm auf. Nach dem Schneebruch hat die Gassendurchforstung immer noch erheblich mehr schwache Stämme als die nicht geschädigte starke Niederdurchforstung.

Figure 8.4 **Stadtforstamt Brilon, Compt 131. Distribution of stems by diameter classes after strip thinning and snow damage in comparison to heavy low thinning.**
In the strip thinning, snow breakage occurred almost exclusively among the weaker trees in the diameter classes of 8-16 cm. After the snow breakage the strip thinning still has considerably more weak stems left than the undamaged heavy low thinning.
Key : N nach Df = number of stems after thinning.
Schneebruch = Snow breakage.
N nach Schneebruch = number of stems after snow breakage.
Gassendf. = strip thinning.
st. Ndf. = heavy low thinning.

durchforstung widersprechen sich. Dieses ist zu erklären durch Unterschiede im Bestandeszustand und dem Zeitabstand zwischen Durchforstung und Eintritt des Schadens (15). Im Winter nach dem Eingriff sind die Bestände besonders labil. Ferner sind eng erwachsene und spät durchforstete Fichtenbestände sehr anfällig, da die Bäume infolge des Engstandes nur kleine Kronen und ein hohes h/d-Verhältnis haben. In unseren Versuchsbeständen, bei denen sehr frühzeitig – im Alter von 20 bis 35 Jahren – jede 4. Reihe entnommen war, hatten die herrschenden Bäume noch ein Kronenprozent von über 50. Hier trat selbst in dem in Niedersachsen extremen Schneebruchwinter 1969/70 kein nennenswerter Schaden auf. Bei unseren Versuchsflächen mit Nieder-, Auslese- und Reihendurchforstung traten bei Auslese- und Reihendurchforstung unbe-

deutend Schäden bei den schwachen Bäumen auf, bei der Niederdurchforstung war kein Schneebruch verursacht, da hier die schwachen gefährdeten Bäume bereits vorher entnommen waren.

Ein besonders drastisches Beispiel bietet der extreme Reihenhieb im Forstamt Brilon, Abt. 131 a. Die starke Durchforstung mit Reihenhieb (Gassenbreite 6 m) und Niederdurchforstung war im Herbst 1969 unmittelbar vor dem Schneebruch durchgeführt worden. Bei der starken Niederdurchforstung trat kein Schneebruchschaden auf, beim Reihenhieb wurden dagegen 18% der Bäume und 10% der Vorrates durch Schnee gebrochen. In Abbildung 8.4 ist die Stammzahlverteilung der Gassendurchforstung (=Reihendurchforstung) und der starken Niederdurchforstung verglichen. Bei der Reihendurchforstung sind im wesentlichen nur die Durchmesserklassen 8,5 bis 16 cm betroffen, also Durchmesserklassen, die bei der starken Durchforstung schon ganz stark reduziert waren. Auch nach dem Schneebruch hat die Reihendurchforstung noch viel mehr schwache Bäume, als die nicht geschädigte Niederdurchforstung. Die wuchskräftigen Zukunftsbäume waren auch bei der geometrischen Durchforstung nicht vom Schneebruch betroffen.

LITERATUR

1. ABETZ, P. (1970). Schwachholzmarkt und waldbauliche Konsequenzen bei Bestandesbegründung und Jungbestandespflege. *Allgemeine Forstzeitschrift.*

2. ÅGREN, A. (1963). *Produktionsföluster till följd av virkestransport i gallringsskog. – Ska vi gallra?* Sveriges Skosvardsförbund, Stockholm S. 30–34.

3. DUMM, G. (1970). Der Einfluß des Verbandes auf Schneebruchgefährdung und Astbildung. *Hessischer Forstverein, Jahresbericht, Schotten 1970,* S. 23–26.

4. GRIESBACH, E. UND MASCHER, E. (1970). *Untersuchungen in stark schneebruchgefährdeten Fichtenbeständen im Südost-Solling.* Seminararbeit d. Forstl. Fakultät der Universität Göttingen.

5. HÜTTE, P. (1967). Die standörtlichen Voraussetzungen der Sturmschäden. *Forstw. Centralblatt,* S. 276.

6. HÜTTE, P. (1969). Investigations concerning the influence of thinnings on the resistance of spruce stands against wind. *Thinning and Mechanizations,* Stockholm, S. 158.

7. FRIES, J. (1969). *Value of residual stand. Principal views. Thinning and Mechanization,* Stockholm, S. 21.

8. FRIES, J. (1973). *Thinning – why and how. Thinning in the Forestry of the Future,* Elmia, Jönköping, Schweden.

9. KRAMER, H. (1968). Zur Behandlung und Beurteilung junger Fichtenbestände. *Allgemeine Forstzeitschrift,* Nr. 28.

10. KRAMER, H. UND BEHRNDT, W. (1969). Maschinelle Streifenläuterung in Fichtenverjüngungen. *Allgemeine Forstzeitschrift,* S. 754–758.

11. KRAMER, H. UND VON KORTZFLEISCH, A. (1970). Erfahrungen mit starker Reihendurchforstung bei Fichte im Westharz. *Der Forst- und Holzwirt,* S. 177–181.

12. KRAMER, H. (1971). Treatment of Young Norway Spruce Stands. *Svensk Skogsvardsförbunds Tidskrift,* S. 281–294.

13. KRAMER, H. (1974). Ertragskundliche und holzmeßkundliche Forschungsergebnisse als Entscheidungshilfen für die forstliche Planung und den laufenden Betrieb. *Allgemeine Forst- und Jagdzeitung,* S. 25–30.

14. KRAMER, H. UND KEUFFEL, W. (1974). Gassendurchforstung. *Allgemeine Forstzeitschrift,* S. 137–140.

15. KRAMER, H. (1974). *Biologische Kriterien als Entscheidungshilfe für die Wahl stark mechanisierter Durchforstungssysteme.* Forstarchiv, S. 217–221.

16. KRAMER, H. (1966). Zur Kulturbegründung und Jungbestandspflege bei Fichte. *Aus dem Walde,* Nr. 12.

17. KRAMER, H. UND PEINE, J. (1968). Erstdurchforstung bei Fichte. *Der Forst- und Holzwirt,* Nr 20.

18. MITSCHERLICH, G. (1968). Zur Frage der Sturmsicherung, der Bestände. *Allgemeine Forstzeitschrift,* Nr. 36/37.

19. MITSCHERLICH, G. (1973). Wald und Wind. *Allgemeine Forst- und Jagdzeitung,* S. 74.

20. NILSON, P. O. UND HYPPELT, A. (1969). *Studies on decays in scars of Norway spruce.* Thinning and Mechanization. IUFRO meeting Royal College of Forestry. Stockholm.

21. PABST VON OHAIN, G. (1974). Rinderverletzungen beim Rücken von Bäumen mit Ästen in schwachen Fichtenbeständen. *Allgemeine Forstzeitschrift,* S. 141–143.

22. PECHMANN, H. VON. (1974). Der Einfluß der Durchforstung auf die Holzqualität, *Forstarchiv,* S. 34–38.

23. PERSSON, P. (1972). Vind-ochsnöskadorssamband med bestandsbehandlingen – inventering av yngre gallringsförsök. *Institutionen för Skogsproduktion, Rapporter och Uppsatser,* Stockholm, Nr. 23.

24. KRAMER, H. (1975). *Erhöhung der Produktionssicherheit zur Förderung einer nachhaltigen Fichtenwirtschaft.* Forstarchiv, S. 9–13.

DISCUSSION

Adlard: These are a series of very interesting experiments. It seems a little difficult to tie them together. It seems to me that it would be better to lay out factorial experiments including type and intensity so that the interaction between these could be evaluated.

Franz: I agree that a factorial design would be much better to answer such questions.

Fries: In Table 6 good revenues were obtained from the removal of two rows in five. Do you intend to thin these treatments selectively at a later stage?

Kramer: Yes. This will involve removing trees from all three remaining rows.

VIEWS ON THE CHOICE OF SILVICULTURAL METHODS AND LOGGING TECHNIQUE IN THINNING

By JÖRAN FRIES

Royal College of Forestry Stockholm, Sweden

1. Introduction

When the harvested wood has to be transported out of the thinned stands, damage is often caused to soil and remaining stand. This damage may be in the form of deep trails caused by the tractors with root damage, rot infections and yield losses as a consequence. The transport may also lead to damage to remaining trees, causing rot infections and decreased quality. The opening up of corridors may also lead to yield losses because of the fact that the corridors are not fully utilized by the remaining stand.

It is important to be able to foresee these losses and to have a knowledge of how they could be limited or avoided. Having this knowledge, it would be possible to choose the combination of silvicultural methods and logging technique giving the best result.

The aim of the project on transport damage, started in 1971 at the Royal College of Forestry, is to give the facts necessary for these considerations. Participating in this project are Dr. Uno Björkhem (soil science), Dr. Arne Hyppel (botanics, mycology), Dr. Göran Lundeberg (botanics, mycology), Dr. Jan Scholander (technique) and Professor Jöran Fries (yield research, economics, project leader). The field work of the project is finished and the work on the publications is under way. This paper is based on results from this project. Preliminary results have earlier been published by Fries (1973) and by Björkhem *et al* (1974).

2. Soil Breakage and Trail Formation

The primary effects of logging by tractor on forest soils are soil breakage and trail formation as well as damage to the tree trunks along the haul-road.

By soil breakage we mean that the humus layer has been torn off from the surrounding untouched humus layer and either been pressed down or crumpled by the wheels or the tracks of the tractor. There is, as could be expected, a strong relationship between trail depth and soil breakage (Figure 9.1). The variation around this relationship is caused to some extent by the fact that even if the soil has a good bearing capacity and thus the trail depth is minor, soil breakage could still be important due to the fact that the humus layer is very thin.

Soil breakage as well as trail depth increase with the number of runs along the road, i.e. with the total amount of transported wood. There is, however, the difference that trail depth after a number of runs seems to reach a fairly constant level (Figure 9.2), while the frequency of soil breakage seems to increase fairly linearly (Figure 9.3). This figure also examplifies the effect of slash from the thinning covering the road. As an average the fre-

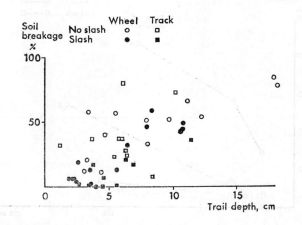

Figure 9.1 Trail depth and soil breakage.

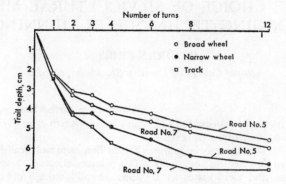

Figure 9.2   Number of turns and trail depth. Tractor: BM Volvo SM 462.

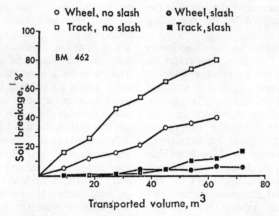

Figure 9.3   Transported volume, and soil breakage. Tractor: BM Volvo SM 462.

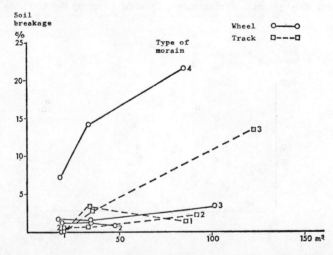

Figure 9.4   Soil breakage as a percent of road length for various total quantities transported along the road and for various types of morain. Type of morain: 1 gravelly, 2 sandy, 3 sandy-loamy, 4 loamy-clayey. Track = track on rear wheels and bogey.

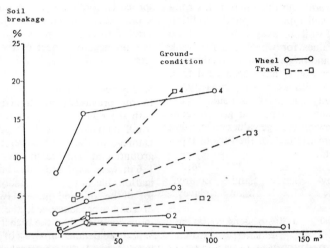

Figure 9.5 Soil breakage as a percent of total road length for various total quantities transported per road and various ground conditions. Ground condition: 1 very good, 2 conditions between 1 and 3, 3 average, 4 conditions between 3 and 5, 5 very bad. Track = track on rear wheels and bogey.

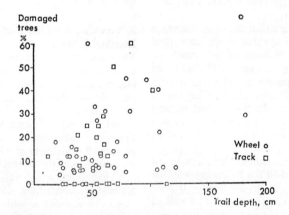

Figure 9.6 Trail depth and damaged trees within 2 m from the trail.

quency of soil breakage has been reduced by 80% by the slash.

The weight of the tractor and the type wheels also have a big influence on the extension of soil damage. Thereby it is rather the specific pressure caused by the wheels and not the total weight of the tractor that is important. A heavy tractor with big wheels could thus cause less damage than a light tractor with small wheels. Tracks on rear wheels and bogie lower the specific soil pressure and increase thereby the bearing capacity. On soils with a good bearing capacity but with a thin humus layer more extensive damage may be caused by tracks than by wheels because of the fact that the metal edges of the track cut the humus layer to pieces.

The extent of the damage is very much dependent on the bearing capacity of the soil. This is clearly shown by observations carried out in connection with practical logging. These studies have been carried out in cooperation with the Logging Research Foundation and consist of observations of about 800 tractor roads with a total length of 76 km. In these studies soil type, ground conditions and soil breakage were recorded. Ground condition which should be an expression of the bearing capacity of the soil is determined by means of soil type and forest type or by means of soil type, soil humidity and climate humidity (Skogsarbeten 1969).

Figures 9.4 and 9.5 show that the amount of soil breakage increases linearly with increased transported quantity of wood and that there is a strong correlation between soil type or ground condition and the amount of soil breakage. It should be observed that the values for wheel and for track (track on rear wheel and bogie) are not directly comparable as tracks apparently have been used to a greater extent on soils with less bearing capacity.

The bearing capacity decreases, as could be expected, with increasing soil type and ground condition class. The following average values concerning ground condition were attained for the various types of moraine in the data.

Type of moraine	1. Gravelly	2. Sandy	3. Sandy-loamy	4. Loamy, clayey
Ground condition	1·06	1·87	2·28	3·50

3. Root Damage and Rot Infections

As could be expected, there is a strong correlation between trail depth and the number of damaged trees (Figure 9.6). By damaged tree we mean a tree which has got at least one root thicker than 2cm damaged by the transport.

The risk of a tree getting a root damaged increases also with the diameter of the tree at the same time as it decreases with the distance of the tree from the trail. Trees standing further away from the tractor trail than two metres are running a very minor risk of getting root damage. The leaving of slash on the roads decreases the risk of road damage considerably. The frequency of damaged trees was twice as high when the road was free of slash as when it was covered with slash.

The risk of rot infection caused by damage on roots may be summarized in the following way for Norway spruce. Damage close to the trees ($<0·5$ m) will in most cases lead to rot in the root as well as in the stem. Damage far away from the trees ($>0·7$–$1·0$ m) may lead to rot in root and stem if the damage is deep, whereas shallow damage that far away from the tree seldom gives rise to any stem infection. Damage to roots smaller than 2 cm seldom gives rise to any rot infection. Corresponding damage on Scots pine seldom leads to rot infection.

4. Yield Losses

Some preliminary results from studies of the effect of transport on yield may be concluded in the following way. The opening up of corridors seems to have had a moderate positive effect on the increment of pine trees close to the roads. For spruce no corresponding effect has been noted. The transport has caused a reduction of the increment close to the roads in the two trials where soil damage and trail formation were important. In both these trials

spruce is dominating. The third trial was made in a pine stand on soil with good bearing capacity. Trail formation here was insignificant and there was no negative effect of the transportation to be seen.

5. Damage to Trunks

In the previously mentioned study in connection with the regular transportations the appearance of trunk damage along the roads was also recorded. Damage to the trunk lower than 1·6 m above the ground and damage inflicted to the trunk above 1·6 m were kept separate. This part of the investigations has not yet been analysed, but as an average for all the collected material two trees in every 100 m of road were damaged, the lower damage being more common than the higher one.

A more detailed analysis of these data has not yet been done. It is, however, apparent that the frequency of stem damage varies with the width of the road, the width of the tractor and its equipment, the number of runs and last but not least the ability of the driver.

6. Views on the Choice of Silvicultural Method and Logging Technique

Through the simulation of stand development, damage and yield in volume and value of various alternatives of stand treatment and logging it will be possible to judge what methods which will yield the best results.

One example of such a simulation is given by Fries in a preliminary summary of the mentioned project (Björkhem *et al* 1974). This example (Table 9.1) shows that the alternatives no thinning and one corridor thinning are very much inferior to those alternatives containing selective thinnings. Furthermore the alternative with one selective thinning is inferior to the alternatives with three thinnings if excessive yield losses could be avoided. On the good site this example is dealing with it is advisable to choose a silvicultural alternative with at least two thinnings, whereby the first one should be a corridor thinning combined with selective thinning and the next and eventually the third one should be purely selective.

The example also shows that if the logging will lead to excessive yield losses and eventually also root damage it should be feasible to avoid this damage by the introduction of more expensive but also less harmful methods, e.g. winching with 80–100 m between the haul-roads. It is assumed that this method does not give a larger extent of stem damage than the other methods.

Based on what is said above concerning the risk of

TABLE 9.1

ALTERNATIVE CHOICES OF THINNING METHODS

Norway spruce, $h_{100}=32$, 2,000 trees per hectare before the first thinning at age 35. Remaining stand at age 80, total yield in m³ and Kr. Sw. at 80 years rotation, present value at the first thinning, calculated with a compound rate of interest of 4% and the value of the first thinning for various treatment- and damage alternatives. By present value is meant net values of all harvests discounted to the time of the first thinning.

| | | No thinning | One selective thinning | One corridor thinning | Three thinnings | | |
| | | | | | Only selective | Corridor thinning +Selective thinning | | |
Alternative No.		1	2	3	4	5[1]	[2]	7[3]
Remaining stand at age 80	mean diameter cm	24·5	29·9	25·2	37·1	38·8	35·9	35·9
	volume, m³	744	659	428	620	584	494	494
Total yield at age 80	m³	744	760	510	824	789	680	680
	%	90	92	62	100	96	83	83
Total yield at age 80	Kr	26 332	30 286	17 912	35 342	34 943	28 267	27 045
	%	74	85	51	100	99	80	77
Present value at age 80	Kr	4 509	5 623	4 980	7 832	7 945	6 548	6 340
	%	58	72	64	100	101	84	81
Net value of the first thinning, Kr		0	670	2 308	313	752	752	752

[1] Insignificant yield losses
[2] Important yield losses
[3] Important yield losses and losses through decay

damage on soils with various bearing capacity, the following guide-lines could be given concerning the choice of logging technique at various ground condition on moraine soil. The use of a heavy forwarder equipped with big rubber tyres, e.g. BM Volvo SM 868 is assumed. See Table 9.2.

According to this example hauling to roads with a distance of 20 m in between should be used on mineral soils with a bearing capacity corresponding to ground condition 1–3. The hauling and transport should be made with a forwarder with big low pressure tyres, e.g. BM Volvo SM 868. If the bearing capacity is inferior winching with a distance of 80–100 m between the haul-roads should be employed. For the transport along the haul-roads the same tractor should be used as in the above-mentioned case, but equipped with tracks on rear wheels and bogie.

TABLE 9.2

EXAMPLES ON THE CHOICE OF LOGGING TECHNIQUE AT VARYING BEARING CAPACITY OF
MINERAL SOILS

Ground condition (mineral soil) (1)	Quantity per road m³	Equipment (2)	Slash (3)	Transport technique (4)
1	0–50	W	–	H
1	50–100	W	–	H
1	100+	W	S	H
2	0–50	W	–	H
2	50–100	W	S	H
2	100+	W	S	H
3	0–50	WT	S	H
3	50–100	T	S	H
3	100+	T	S	HW (HF)
4	0–50	T	S	W (HF)
4	50–100	T	S	W (HF)
4	100+	T	S	W (HF)
5	0+	T	S	W (HF)

Explanations
(1) Ground condition
    1. Very good
    2. Conditions between 1 and 3
    3. Average
    4. Conditions between 3 and 5
    5. Very bad
(2) Equipment
    W =wheels
    T   =track on rear wheels and bogie
    WT=wheels ev with tracks on rear wheels and bogie
(3) Slash
    S=the road should be covered with slash
(4) Transportation technique
    H   =hauling with around 20 m between the haul-roads
    W =winching with about 100 m between the haul-roads
    HW=hauling or winching
    HF =hauling if the soil is frozen

REFERENCES

FRIES, J. (1973). *Thinning – why and how?* – Reprint of papers from the International conference at ELMIA 1973 *Thinning in the forestry of the future.* Department of Operational Efficiency, Royal College of Forestry. Garpenberg, Sweden.

BJÖRKHEM, U., FRIES, J., HYPPEL, A., LUNDEBERG, G. AND SCHOLANDER, J. (1974). Damage by heavy vehicles in thinnings. – *Journal of the Royal Academy of Agriculture and Forestry*, 1974. Stockholm.

DISCUSSION

Malcom: Were you talking about permanent extraction roads or temporary extraction racks?

Fries: These are corridors opened up in the stand. I could not say whether they would be used once or several times. The investigations however, were made after they were used just once. This is a good question because if you carry out repeated logging in these corridors then the damage might be even more serious.

Malcolm: In Britain something like 40% of the soils which we are concerned with have some degree of impeded drainage and I think it extremely important that some attention be paid to this. What you call soil breakage, disturbance of the humus horizons, in fact may be a good thing in some conifer stands, but it is the soil compaction on fine textured soils that is important and I do not think we know anything about the recovery of soils which have been compacted.

Fries: We have given some thought to this and I know from agricultural experience that compaction can have quite bad effects. I also know from experiments in Holland, where seedlings were planted in compacted soils. The roots did not penetrate at a certain degree of compaction but remained on the surface. We have also had an example from Sweden in a military area where there was very heavy traffic. Here there were undoubtedly large losses due to compaction. In forest soils we don't know whether frost will break up compacted soils.

Malcolm: If the roots are incapable of penetrating soil of high density then they remain on the surface. Surface traffic can then affect the surface feeding root system.

Stratmann: You tested a wheeled tractor and a half track tractor. Did you test a full track machine?

Fries: No, we used only the two you have mentioned. There is of course a tendency that on soils with a lower bearing capacity for tracks to cause less damage than wheels. However, on very sturdy soils with a thin humus layer the tracks might cut through the thinned humus layer and thus cause more soil breakage than wheels.

THE INFLUENCE OF DIFFERENT THINNING SYSTEMS ON DAMAGE TO SOIL AND TREES

By HENRY A. FROEHLICH

Associate Professor of Forest Engineering Oregon State University, Corvallis, Oregon

Damage to soil and residual trees while thinning young forest stands has been of increasing concern. This concern parallels the increase of mechanization of the thinning process. Soil damage as discussed in this paper is taken as any impact on soil which reduces the potential growth of residual trees or of the seedlings to be established at the conclusion of the thinning cycle. Tree damage is taken to be any impact on tree boles or roots which is sufficient to reduce tree growth either directly through physical damage or indirectly through the introduction of wood rotting fungi.

At the 1969 IUFRO conference in Stockholm on thinning and mechanization, recent reports given at the ELMIA conference in Jönköping, and in the research literature of Europe and America, a wide array of responses to soil and stem damage is reported. Some of the data seems conflicting and it is disappointing to note that we still are not able to predict what growth response to expect from a given level of impact. It is relatively easy to measure the extent of soil disturbance, degree of compaction or number and size of tree wounds. It is obviously much more difficult to measure the actual impact of these factors on tree growth. We need to recognise that tree damage as expressed in number, size and location of wounds is only an index to possible rot infection and subsequent wood fibre losses. Likewise, measured soil disturbance or compaction is only an index to possible growth impacts. Since it is unlikely that we can intensively manage forests without causing some disturbance, especially with increased ground-based mechanization, it is important to separate actual damage from simple visual effects.

The highly variable results observed in soil and stem damage studies appears to be largely due to the high variability that exists in site, stand and operational factors. It is not possible to consider only the thinning system without examining the other two.

Site factors would include:
   (1) topography
   (2) soil type and depth
   (3) soil moisture at time of thinning
   (4) degree of soil protection from litter or slashings

Stand factors would include:
   (1) tree species
   (2) age or size
   (3) stand density before and after thinning
   (4) seasonal differences in bark strength
   (5) rooting characteristics

Operation factors would include:
   (1) ground pressure and vibration of equipment
   (2) operator skill and attitude for given type of equipment
   (3) product size (loadsize) being removed
   (4) pattern of extraction routes
   (5) frequency of entry

Some generalities I have drawn from the scattered research results are illustrated in Figure 10.1. In this diagram the three elements of site, stand and operations are arranged in a fashion that illustrate the trends evident from much of the research.

Soil compactibility is most strongly characterized by soil texture and soil moisture and might represent major site factors. We could also indicate increasing slope as a site factor which tends to cause increasing soil disturbance.

The stand factors most often recorded are related to the tree species' susceptibility to damage. Thus it may be possible to rank species from relatively resistant to most sensitive to root damage or soil compaction. In the Pacific Northwest, we might place Ponderosa pine or lodgepole pine at the relatively resistant end of the scale followed by Douglas-fir, Sitka spruce and Western hemlock towards the most sensitive end of the scale.

The effect of the thinning system on soil and tree damage may be most strongly related to the compactive energy applied to the soil surface. Here we see some differences created by small crawler tractors with bearing pressures of 3–4 psi compared with rubber-tyred skidders with ground pressures of 25–30 psi.

Very little work has been reported which shows the relative impact of different thinning systems on direct tree damage. In my recent measurements, as shown in Table 10.1, the differences in tree wounding even between cable and crawler tractor appeared to be relatively small.

Some of the research results clearly indicate that

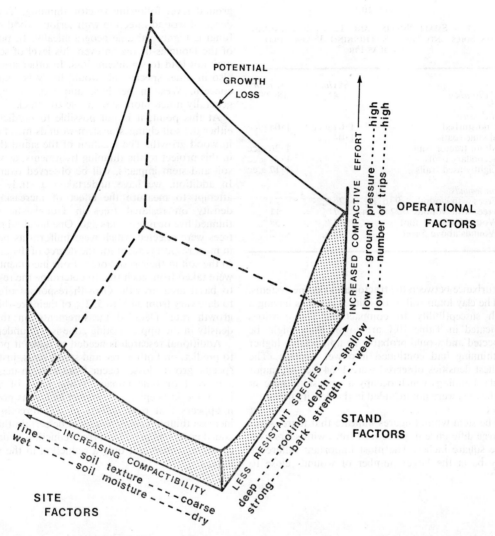

POTENTIAL GROWTH LOSS

INCREASED COMPACTIVE EFFORT —
low - - - -ground pressure - - - - -high
low - - - -number of trips - - - - -high

OPERATIONAL FACTORS

LESS RESISTANT SPECIES
shallow - - -rooting depth - - -deep
weak - - - -bark strength - - - -strong

STAND FACTORS

fine - - - - INCREASING COMPACTIBILITY - - - - coarse
wet - - - - soil texture
soil moisture - - - - dry

SITE FACTORS

Figure 10.1 Inter-relationship of factors affecting potential reduction in tree growth following thinning.

growth losses do occur and in some cases seriously offset the gains from thinning. Therefore, most of us operate under the concept that the least compaction and the least scarring of residual trees the better. Much of the research has been on thinning operations as normally used by the industry. Relatively few workers have attempted to determine just how much the impact could be reduced by specially designing the thinning system to this end.

Elsewhere in this Bulletin, Professor Aulerich reports on the effort to measure the economic differences between a small skyline system and crawler tractors used in thinning a 35-year old Douglas-fir stand. Soil and tree factors were also measured and the results are shown in Table 10.1.

The soil on this site is a Nekia clay loam, averaging 30 inches in depth. The thinning took place during dry weather with soil moisture ranging from 20% to 30% during the thinning operation.

The small crawler tractor used for thinning had a static ground pressure of 5·3 pounds per square inch. Logs were ground-skidded without the use of an arch or other lifting system. The skyline system was not designed to provide lift to the logs beyond that necessary for ease in yarding. However, the logs tended to ride up over the slash and only occasionally gouged into the soil. This factor accounts for the large difference in surface soil

TABLE 10.1

IMPACTS OF SMALL SKYLINE AND TRACTOR THINNING ON SOILS AND TREES IN THINNING 35-YEAR OLD DOUGLAS-FIR

	Skyline	*Tractor*
Soil disturbed	4%	18–28%
Soil density		
Undisturbed	1·04 g/cc	1·04 g/cc
Skyline roads	1·04 g/cc	—
Major tractor trails	—	1·26 g/cc
Secondary trails	—	1·21 g/cc
Lightly used trails	—	1·17 g/cc
Stem wounds		
Trees with wounds >9 sq. in.	26%	28%
Trees with wounds >72 sq. in.	7%	11%
Wounds below 1 foot	33%	58%
Wounds above 5 feet	22%	2%

disturbance between the tractor and skyline systems.

The clay loam soil of this site is rated as having a high susceptibility to compaction. The densities indicated in Table 10.1 are lower than might be expected and would probably be appreciably higher if thinning had continued into wet weather. The highest densities observed were 1·64 g/cc on major trails. Landings which occupy a very small percent of the area were not included in the density measurement.

The stem wound figures indicate that there is not a large difference in percent of trees with scars over nine square inches. The most important difference may be in the larger number of wounds close to

ground level following tractor thinning. The incidence of wound infection with serious wood rotting fungi is highly variable geographically. In portions of the Douglas-fir region even this level of scarring may not lead to significant loss. In other areas and also in other species this would likely be cause for concern. Western hemlock and Sitka spruce are generally much more susceptible to attack.

At this point, it is not possible to predict what either the soil changes or stem wounds mean in loss in wood growth. The reaction of the stand thinned in this project to the thinning treatments, as well as soil and stem impacts, will be observed over time. In addition, we have undertaken a study in an attempt to measure the effect of increasing soil density on residual trees in Douglas-fir stands thinned five or more years ago. One hundred sample trees were selected which were uniform as possible in most respects except for the degree of disturbance to the soil in their root zones. Four increment cores were taken from each tree to determine the response to basal area growth. Growth responses observed to date vary from 34% to 552% of their pre-thinning growth rate. Detailed measurements on the soil density in the upper rooting zone is still underway.

Additional research is needed to make it possible to predict, on both a tree and stand basis, just what specific growth losses occur from a given degree of soil, root or bole impact. While most of us are interested in keeping any impact as low as possible, it appears that most efforts in this direction will increase thinning costs. We must be certain that any added costs will produce a true reduction in damage to soil and trees not only a reduction in the visible impact.

DISCUSSION

Fries: I think Figure 10.1 is an admirable way of explaining some of the correlation between factors but the fact that you have included not one factor but several on each access illustrates how complex this situation is. To take account of each of them would mean a multi-dimensional figure. This means that the only way to study the problem is in some way factorial.

Froehlich: This diagram is a sort of plea for future researchers to include these variables or to account for them in some fashion in reporting, such that one might be better able to translate it. It was very complex.

Fox: Is it correct to say that with the sky-line you had 78% of wounds occurring below 5 ft?

Froehlich: Yes. The location of the wound means that the trees are obviously close to the extraction routes. Removing these trees at the next thinning means widening of the corridor rather than a selective thinning and consequently flexibility in future thinnings is greatly reduced.

Fries: In our project we have developed a device to measure the density of the soil. It is a kind of needle about 1 cm thick with which you penetrate the soil and record the pressure put on the device as well as the degree of penetration. You then get a curve showing how the soil varies in density.

Froehlich: This is something like a penetrometer. We found that the stoniness of the ground we were working on made this very difficult but certainly with a uniform soil it would be highly desirable.

Kramer: How serious are the wounds in terms of economics?

Froehlich: The economic effect would be related to some wood quality loss in the stem but I visualise that in many cases healing would prevent serious effects. Wounds would become more important where they affected the highest quality peeler logs.

W. Sutton: In New Zealand we have found with Douglas fir and *Pinus radiata* that wounds in the upper part of the tree are more important than those occurring at the base for two reasons. One is that the defects caused at the bottom of the stem tend to be lost in slabs. Secondly the tree appears to have a more active defensive mechanism in the lower half of the stem than in the upper part.

Froehlich: I think this depends on specific fungi, some of which are more prevalent in the lower regions of the stem, others in the upper regions.

THE MACHINES ARE COMING, THE MACHINES ARE COMING

By HAROLD E. YOUNG

School of Forest Resources
University of Maine
Orono, Maine 04473 USA

Introduction

Approximately ten years ago an extremely humorous American film was first shown publicly. It was "The Russians are Coming, the Russians are Coming". I have quite obviously based the title of this paper on the title of that film. There are more important reasons for doing so. In the film a Russian submarine with mechanical problems is forced to send a few men ashore on the New England coast of the USA. The local townspeople are certain that it is an invasion. A series of humorous incidents lead to a confrontation which is forgotten as Americans and Russians join forces to rescue a child precariously hung on a church roof. Then the townspeople in an array of fishing and pleasure boats safely led the Russian submarine out to sea despite the ominous threat of American military aircraft.

I see a parallel situation as forest harvesting machines are being developed for both thinning and harvesting purposes. There is already an outcry of damage to regeneration, increased soil erosion and deterioration of the site by removal of a greater amount of the available nutrient supply from the forest ecosystem. The outcry, in my judgment, is possibly more an outrage against a highly mechanized system than justifiable cause for alarm about the forest ecosystem. I believe that as we learn to use the new types of machines we will learn how to protect the forest ecosystem. Eventually, as in the case of the film, those who are now alarmed will staunchly defend the thinning and harvesting machines.

Forty years ago this fall I transferred to the University of Maine as a second year forestry student. Almost immediately I became aware of silviculture treatments called thinnings that would permit professional foresters to control the quality and species composition of the forest crop. Virtually in the same breath the professor made it clear that particularly in younger stands that such thinnings were "pre-commercial" and therefore the costs could seldom be justified. This same philosophy was expressed as recently as the meeting of this Working Party in Nancy in June 1973. I had the temerity then to suggest that the development of proper machines and utilization of the material harvested could eliminate the "pre-commercial" notion from

our professional vocabulary. At that time absolutely no consideration was given to my views.

It is the purpose of this paper to briefly sketch historical developments in forestry, to present the case for the Complete Tree Concept and its most recent evolutionary developments and to present the case for thinning machines that are already here today and for those being developed.

Forestry History

Evidences of forestry practices go back to pre-biblical times with simplified regulation appearing in England nearly a thousand years ago. Serious national concern about an impending wood shortage in England is very evident in Sir John Evelyn's monumental work, Sylva, which appeared in 1668. The establishment of the forestry masters schools in Germany in the latter part of the eighteenth century (Heske 1938), the forerunners of the forestry schools, confirms national commitment to widespread applications of forest management. It was only a short time later that Cotta (1817) admonished the forester by writing "Our foresters can still be divided into empiricists and scientists, rarely are both united". Unfortunately his remarks are as appropriate today as they were then.

For some, forestry begins with the seed and ends with the harvest. However for many, including the writer, forestry begins with the seed and extends to the public who consumes the manufactured product and who uses the forest for clean air, clean water and recreation. Thus there are four dimensions of forestry: forest science, forest management, manufacture and sale of forest products and the social use of the forest. There is very little communication between these four dimensions of forestry. In fact an objective assessment shows that these four dimensions exist virtually independent of each other despite philosophic policy statements that imply a close working relationship between them. If Heinrich von Cotta were alive today and preparing, let us say, the twentieth edition of his *Silviculture* I am confident that he would admonish with great force and clarity the four dimensions of forestry, as he did the two dimensions 161 years ago, for failing to become intimate with each other for mutual benefit and the long-range survival of our society.

Even though some may decry the situation as I have depicted it none can deny the essence of my sketch. Forest scientists armed only with axes demonstrated as much as two hundred years ago that by thinning, the density, species composition and quality of the forest can be controlled. The practising forester has seldom been able to apply this because of the cost of thinning and the absence of markets for the harvested material. Unfortunately the practising forester has kept away from both equipment developers and manufacturers. At the same time manufacturers have only used more of a usable species or added species to the usable list when their supply was threatened. In other words the manufacturers have kept away from the foresters. Although I am obviously critical of this mutual indifference, this system, if it can be called a system, did work reasonably well for a very long time. It is my contention that this system is totally inadequate for our small world with a more or less fixed forest base and a rapidly expanding human population.

The Complete Tree Concept
The Complete Tree Concept (Young 1964) is: biological and technological investigation of the entire tree from the root tips to the leaf hairs inclusive. With the inclusion of shrubs, successional species and seedlings and saplings of commercially used species this concept was extended into the Complete Forest Concept. Then it evolved into woody fibre production, production and use of vegetation on right-of-ways and more recently into the commercial use of thinnings, a topic which will be dealt with separately at the end of this section. When the Complete Tree Concept came into focus the major products considered were boards, paper, paperboard, particleboard and fibreboard illustrating the major solid and reconstituted uses of wood. This list has been expanded within the past five years to include wood, bark and leaves or needles as food for animal and human consumption, organic compounds, fuel for power plants, a primary source of ethanol and methanol and mulch on right-of-ways and gardens. To this imposing list of uses of forest products must be added at the very top the primary uses of forest ecosystems for mankind which are clean air, clean water and recreation.

My publications have repeatedly stressed the importance of a continuous exchange of information between the specialists constituting the four dimensions of forestry. It is more than mutual benefit; it is mutual survival. Two illustrations will hopefully bring this salient point to the foreground. Shioga (1967) states that as a result of extensive and repeated forest fires plus very bad forest land practices, all of which took place more than a thousand years ago,

portions of China amounting to millions of acres are still barren wasteland. It not only could happen anywhere it could happen here. Kelly (1967) states that in 1962 a plant scientist and an agricultural engineer culminated ten years of plant and machine development by producing a practical tomato harvester. That could also happen in our forests. The first illustration demonstrates the irreparable damage that could result if our forests are destroyed by neglect and indifference. For emphasis may I point out again that such a sad state of affairs would not only reduce our supply of raw material for industrial products but would also reduce our supply of clean air, clean water and recreation. The second illustration demonstrates the optimum of cooperation between plant growers (may I remind you that a tree is merely a long lived plant) and technologists. A continuous flow of information between forest scientists and managers and between engineers and marketing specialists is essential for the perpetual survival and health of our society. The lack of such cooperation can assure the downfall of society as we know it today.

Thinnings
The puckerbrush pulping studies (Case *et al.* 1973) established that seedlings and saplings of hardwood commercial tree species as well as the non-commercial hardwood shrub and tree species can be used to produce usable pulp. In most instances pulp made from everything above ground (bark on stem and all of the small branches) is mixed with hardwood chips without bark ranging from 10–50% puckerbrush depending on the quality of pulp being manufactured. This has already been extended by Morey (1974) as a technique for thinning less desirable species and defective trees in hardwood stands ranging from up to 60 feet in height that will eventually produce sawtimber. Morey has demonstrated that such thinnings provide an income to the landowner, provide a net profit to the operator of a Morbark Chiparvestor system and provide acceptable material for a hardwood pulpmill. It has been reported on a casual basis that similar thinnings have been conducted on softwood stands. To determine the yield and physical characteristics of thinning material in stands for seven softwood species and the biomass of thinning material that might be removed during the life of the stand a study was initiated in the summer of 1974 at the University of Maine. Preliminary results are given in Table 11.1. Table 11.2 shows the range in stand density and biomass in representative plots of natural softwood stands, mainly of spruce and fir. Smith (1974) has suggested that the biomass in thinnings over the life of the stand may equal the tonnage of the merchant-

able bole. Final results should be available by 1976.

Complete Tree Utilization

The philosophy behind application of the Complete Tree Concept is: use as much of the standing vegetation as possible to minimize waste consonant with the principles of forest ecology. This means that the forest ecosystem must not be allowed to deteriorate as a result of harvesting by the prevention of erosion and by fertilizing, when necessary, to maintain a reasonable nutrient supply.

At the present time the harvesting industry uses such terms as "whole tree, tree length, full tree and total tree" when they only mean the above ground portion of the tree (Keays 1971 and Keays and Hatton 1972). The implication of these words to the general public is that the entire tree is harvested when in fact the above ground portion is only 75% of the

TABLE 11.1

PARTIAL RESULTS OF THE PULPING PHASE OF THE SOFTWOOD THINNINGS STUDY

GREEN

Species Pulped	Perman-ganate Number	Pulp Yield (%)			Grams of Active Alkali Consumed Per 100 Grams of Material
		Total	Acceptable	Rejects	
Norway Spruce WOOD	23·5	46·1	46·1	0	13·1
„ „ Stem	30·4	42·0	39·8	2·2	14·5
„ „ Top	36·2	32·8	29·0	3·8	16·0
„ „ Whole	31·5	38·0	34·9	3·1	15·6
Red Pine Stem	22·6	40·9	40·1	0·8	14·6
„ „ Top	22·6	29·3	28·8	0·5	15·5
„ „ Whole	27·7	37·1	35·5	1·6	15·9
Eastern Larch Stem	30·7	40·4	38·3	2·1	15·6
„ „ Top	35·6	33·2	29·5	3·7	16·3
„ „ Whole	30·3	40·1	35·5	3·6	15·7
Eastern Hemlock Stem	32·1	41·1	40·4	0·7	14·6
„ „ Top	35·0	33·6	32·4	1·2	16·1
„ „ Whole	32·7	38·3	37·5	0·8	14·8
White Cedar Stem	29·1	43·2	42·0	1·2	14·7
„ „ Top	34·2	35·6	34·4	1·2	15·8
„ „ Whole	33·4	40·6	39·6	1·0	15·9
White Pine Stem	29·5	42·4	40·6	1·8	16·3
„ „ Top	35·5	29·0	27·6	1·4	17·0
„ „ Whole	28·5	38·5	35·4	3·1	15·9
Balsam Fir Stem	33·2	43·2	40·8	2·4	16·5
„ „ Top	37·2	34·8	33·1	1·7	16·9
„ „ Whole	34·8	35·6	33·8	1·8	16·2

DRY

Species Pulped	Perman-ganate Number	Total	Acceptable	Rejects	Grams of Active Alkali Consumed Per 100 Grams of Material
Norway Spruce Whole	31·7	39·3	34·8	4·5	15·4
Red Pine Whole	28·3	36·0	32·5	3·5	16·0
Eastern Larch Whole	31·6	40·7	35·5	5·2	16·1
White Cedar Whole	34·0	40·3	36·5	3·8	15·9
Eastern Hemlock Whole	32·4	41·7	39·9	1·8	15·2
White Pine Whole	28·1	38·6	36·5	2·1	15·2
Balsam Fir Whole	34·3	37·6	34·9	2·7	15·6

NOTES: 1. Stem is defined as wood and bark of the bole from the stump to the first live branch.
2. Top is defined as wood, bark and needles from the first live branch to the tip.
3. Whole is defined as wood, bark and needles proportionate to weight of stem and top.

TABLE 11.2

REPRESENTATIVE PLOTS SHOWING RANGE IN STAND DENSITY AND BIOMASS ON THE THINNINGS STUDIES OF NATURAL SOFTWOOD STANDS THAT ARE PRIMARILY SPRUCE AND FIR*

Age (years)	Height (metres)	Stems per hectare 2·5 cm. (DBH) and larger				Above ground biomass cubic metre equivalents per hectare				Below ground biomass cubic metre equivalents per hectare				Total biomass – above and below ground cubic metre equivalents per hectare			
		Leave	Cut	Standing Dead	Total	Leave	Cut	Standing Dead	Total	Leave	Cut	Standing Dead	Total	Leave	Cut	Standing Dead	Total
60	18	930	1,860	232	3,022	456	237	4	697	120	71	1	192	576	308	5	889
60	19	697	2,557	2,092	5,346	102	134	52	288	29	37	16	82	181	171	68	370
75	16	1,627	3,952	1,860	7,439	300	232	31	563	92	65	7	164	392	297	38	727
57	14	1,162	8,137	2,325	11,624	149	338	33	520	43	84	7	134	192	422	40	654
55	11	1,500	9,500	6,000	17,000	70	196	34	300	20	57	9	86	90	253	43	386
27	10	2,500	12,250	5,000	19,750	136	192	22	350	27	46	5	78	163	238	27	428
24	7	12,500	12,500	7,500	32,500	106	106	35	247	30	30	9	69	136	136	44	316
13	3	45,000	45,000	—	90,000	281	281	—	562	75	75	—	150	356	356	—	712

*43 plots to date

Complete Tree. In other words for every three tons or three cord equivalents removed by the most modern harvesting machines, The Morbark Chiparvestors, one ton or one cord equivalent is left in the ground as the stumproot system.

The Chiparvestor type of harvesters is a large mobile machine. A single operator controls a boom that places the entire stem and branch section of a tree on a platform near the chipper with the chips blown directly into a van at the back side of the machine. This machine can handle boles up to 20 inches in diameter and can average 120 tons of chips in an eight-hour day. The Morbark Industries Company has an assembly line completing one machine a day and may have as many as three assembly lines producing a machine a day of different size classes within a year. It is likely that between 5 and 7% of all chips for reconstituted products will come from such machines this year and it is very possible that such machines will produce as much as 60% of the chips for reconstituted products within ten years.

Koch (1974) has developed a successful prototype to sever the lateral roots and to remove the main taproot of southern pines. It can be used in place of a feller-buncher or it can be used where the boles have previously been harvested. Although untested to date for species with a diversified root system typical of the central and north temperate zones there are no obvious reasons why it should not work as well there.

It is already apparent that smaller self-propelled harvesters requiring only a single operator will shortly be in demand. These should be able to commercially clearcut puckerbrush on right-of-ways and other areas and to thin stands of trees up to eight inches in diameter at ground level. The Vecoplan Company, a German firm, has developed a prototype that fulfils these requirements except for cutting the tree. It can pick up previously felled trees which are fed directly into a drum type chipper and then the chips go directly to a van. One or more companies in each of the Scandinavian countries is also experimenting along these lines. No doubt we will eventually have a complete array of size classes of mobile and self-propelled harvesters to accommodate a wide variety of management objectives and terrain conditions. It appeals to common sense that large manufacturers of farm, forestry and highway equipment are sensitive to this rapidly expanding market. No doubt they are already developing and testing prototypes but will make no public announcements of their achievements until their harvesters are available for sales and sales promotion.

The Palleri Stumparvester (Hakkila and Makela 1973) was developed in Finland to be used in swamps to reduce the stump-root system to smaller pieces after removing it from a peat bog. Stone and earth are not a major problem in swamp forests but will be a technical problem in order to commercially remove the stump-root system of trees growing in soil. Koch reduced this problem by severing the lateral roots. Believing that such a problem can be solved is already going a long way towards solving such a problem.

One American and one Scandinavian firm are already interested in developing a Complete Tree harvester which will, by definition, include the stump-root system. The first generation of Complete Tree harvesters most likely will appear before 1980 with, no doubt, an improved second generation within the next five years.

Ecologically sound forest management demands regeneration methods appropriate to each particular site. On right-of-ways and certain forest areas, coppicing, the development of shoots from the stump, may be the preferred method of regeneration. It would be foolish to remove the stump-root system on such sites and it might be equally true on steep hillsides covered with fragile soils. In sharp contrast to such situations would be portions of the southeast where the present practice is to remove and burn the stump-root system before planting. There the use of the stump-root system could convert a sizable cost into a profit.

It must be pointed out that increased mechanization will:

(a) reduce the forest work force.
(b) require machine operators of greater skill and increased training.
(c) change from piece rate to hourly rate with bonus.
(d) move in the direction of year-round employment with increased benefits to employee.
(e) increased value of employees with increased years of service.

Complete Tree Biological Studies

In the past ten years there has been an exponential increase in the number of biomass and nutrient studies that have been published. As an illustration of this, there were eight papers presented in a Symposium on Primary Productivity and Mineral Cycling in Natural Ecosystems in 1967, 16 papers on Forest Biomass Studies were presented at the IUFRO Congress in 1971 and there were 39 papers presented in IUFRO Biomass Studies in 1973. These attest not only to the number of studies in the techniques of conducting biomass and nutrient studies but also are indicative of the application of these measures to assess biological processes in trees.

There are more individual biological studies in

progress than individual technological studies of processes and harvesting equipment within the Complete Tree Concept. The reason is quite simple. There are more biological research centres comprising a much greater scientific staff than there are in the staffs of a fewer number of technological centres. The effectiveness of the latter group is so strong that one must assume that the two halves of the concept are progressing at about the same rate.

Integrated Studies

Much, but fortunately not all, of the effort referred to in the two previous sections has been entirely industrially oriented or entirely biologically oriented. Those studies are not complying with the spirit of the Complete Tree Concept in which a constant exchange of information within the biological half and within the technological half as well as between the two halves. The importance of exchanging information between the two halves cannot be over emphasized.

An integrated study, as I define one, is a combination of biology and technology in the planning phase, experimental phase and writing phase. These studies should involve forest scientists and forest technologists who are interested in obtaining new information and who then are concerned with industrial applications. Some of the most staunch supporters of this approach are: Keays and his associates in the Canadian Forestry Service; Hakkila and his associates in the Finnish Forest Research Institute; Steinbeck and his associates in Georgia; Auchter, Koch and associates in the U.S. Forest Service; Benson, Einspahr and associates of the Institute of Paper Chemistry; and Young, Chase and associates in Maine. Their studies have been characterized by interest in the biomass and technological potential of shrubs and trees; above ground in all cases and below ground in some.

Summary and Forecast

In the past ten years there have been a number of separate biological, technological and integrated studies within the Complete Tree Concept. These have yielded so much information on the total availability in the standing forest and the possibilities of using bark, branches and leaves or needles and the stump-root system that commercial applications already exist at a number of mills manufacturing a variety of reconstituted products. Harvesting machines, such as the Morbark Total Tree Chiparvestor, are being used for above ground portion of trees and the Palleri Stumparvester has been developed to utilize the stump-root system in swamps. Smaller self-propelled harvesting machines are on the drawing boards in equipment companies in several countries. This portends a future with harvesting machines ranging in size from one man-one machine system to large machines in a multi-machine system for clearcutting to thinning under terrain conditions ranging from steep rocky slopes to swamps.

The future is both challenging and exciting. We must learn the upper limits of dry matter production for forests by region and site conditions. Even with the most advanced forest management that will include fertilization and genetics, there will be forest production limits. When these limits are established, it will be essential for human society to restrict its appetite for growth and development accordingly if human society is to continue with present living standards. In addition to a variety of forest products, our forests provide much of our clean air, clean water and recreation. Harvesting systems must be developed that will minimize if not eliminate damage to the forest ecosystem in order to maintain the nutrient vitality. To accomplish this tremendous undertaking, we must expand integrated research and the application of such research within the Complete Tree Concept. This must be a fact rather than a dream by the end of the century and as an incurable optimist I really think it will be.

LITERATURE CITED

AUCHTER, R. J. (1972). Pulping without barking increases fiber yield. *Pulp and Paper*. June. p. 46.

BENSON, M. K. AND EINSPAHR, D. W. (1972). *Yields from 18 year-old aspen via total tree harvesting*. Genetics and Physiology Notes No. 14. Institute of Paper Chemistry, Wisconsin.

CHASE, A. J., HYLAND, F. AND YOUNG, H. E. (1973). *The commercial potential of puckerbrush pulp*. Tech. Bul. 65. Life Sciences and Agr. Exp. Sta., University of Maine.

COTTA, H. (1817). Anweisung zum Waldbau 1st ed. preface translated in *Forestry Quarterly*. 1:3–5.

EVELYN, J. (1670). *Sylva* 2nd ed. p. 245.

HESKE, F. (1938). *German Forestry*. Yale University Press New Haven, Conn. p. 342.

HAKKILA, P. (1971). Branches, stumps and roots as a future raw material source in Finland. In *Forest Biomass Studies* (H. Young, ed.). p. 51–62.

HAKKILA, P. AND MAKELA, M. (1973). Harvesting of stump and root wood by the Palleri Stumparvester. *Com. Inst. Forest. Fenniae*. 77.5.

KEAYS, J. L. (1971). *Complete tree utilization – An analysis of the literature information reports VP-C-69, 70, 71, 77, 79*. Western Forest Products Laboratory, Vancouver, B.C., Canada.

KEAYS, J. L. AND HATTON, J. V. (1972). Complete Tree utilization studies. II. The yield and quality of kraft pulp from the components of *Picea glauca*. *Tappi*. 54(10)1721.

KELLY, C. F. (1967). Mechanical harvesting. *Scientific American*. 217:50–59.

KOCH, P. (1974). Whole-tree harvesting of pines with taproot attached. *Southern Lumberman*. 228:13–14.

MOREY, H. (1974). Personal communication.

SHIOGA, T. (1967). A short history of forestry and forestry research in eastern Asia. In *International Forestry Review* Vol. 2:1–36. Romberger and Mikola, ed.

SMITH, D. M. (1974). *Impact of forest management practices*. In a symposium on availability of residuals to be published by American Institute of Chemical Engineers; 1974 national meeting in Pittsburgh.

STEINBECK, K. AND MAY, J. T. (1971). Productivity of very young *Plantanus occidentalis*. In *Forest Biomass Studies*. p. 152–164. H. Young, ed.

YOUNG, H. E. (1964). The Complete Tree concept – a challenge and an opportunity. *Proc. Soc. Amer. For*. p. 231–233.

————. (1967). *Symposium on primary productivity and mineral cycling in natural ecosystems*. H. Young, ed. University of Maine Press.

————. (1971). *Forest Biomass Studies* (working party on forest biomass of Section 25, IUFRO). H. Young, ed. University of Maine Press.

————. (1973). *IUFRO Biomass Studies* (Working party on forest biomass of IUFRO). H. Young, ed. University of Maine Press.

DISCUSSION

Van Laar: Is it necessary to increase fertilisation because the whole tree is utilised?

Young: I am more interested in the nutrient cycle, but obviously the more of the tree you use the more nutrient you take from the forest. I don't know any place in the world where we really have a good assessment of the available nutrient pool in a given locality. There have been studies in Europe and some that I am undertaking suggesting that about half the nutrient requirements come from rain. In fact, if we never cut a tree more nutrients will flow into the sea every year than are tied up in the biomass. Certainly we may have to add to the nutrient pool but there are other things which are worthy of even greater concern than the loss of nutrient.

Fries: I recall a trial in northern Sweden where in a clear felled area branches were removed from half the area but left in the other half. The area was restocked with spruce. In the sixth year after planting the area on which the branches had been left showed a substantially greater height increment than in the remaining area. This does not necessarily mean that we should try to retain branches but we should encourage research into this field. In this case it might not have been the effect of nutrients but perhaps a mulching effect that accounted for the difference in heights.

Bredberg: A series of experiments in Sweden show that it is probably less of a danger on the very best soils but the loss of nutrients is more a problem of the poor sites. This means that on the best sites for both technical and biological reasons whole tree utilisation could be employed. This is one of the few cases where technical biological and economic requirements all fit together.

W. Sutton: I am all for maximum utilisation and while maximum volume production is important, quality is no less important. If the bottom half of the tree is worth 30 times as much as the roots or the leaves it is better that we should try to obtain more of that part, even if it means a loss somewhere else in the tree.

Paper 12

DIE DURCHFORSTUNGSTECHNIK ALS MITTEL UND PROBLEM EINER PFLEGLICHEN WALDBEWIRTSCHAFTUNG
erörtert am Beispiel der Fichte

Von S. HÄBERLE*

Institut fur Waldarbeit und Forstmachinenkunde der Universität Gottingen

Gegenstand meiner Ausführungen ist die "Durchforstungstechnik". Darunter verstehe ich die Art der waldbaulichen Bestandesbehandlung ebenso wie "Technik" im Sinne von "Technologie" oder "Arbeitsverfahren".

Als Koordinaten der Durchforstungstechnik fungieren drei Zielsphären:

Die Sphäre 1 wird bestimmt durch das Globalziel, im Umtriebsalter volbestockte Flächen möglichst wertvollen und stark dimensionierten Holzes zu haben.

Bei der Durchforstung schauen wir unter solchem Blickwinkel allein auf den verbleibenden Bestand, und zwar sollen hier die Durchforstungsmaßnahmen im einzelnen.

(a) die Qualität des Bestandes erhöhen und
(b) den verbleibenden Bäumen mehr Wuchsraum verschaffen.

Die Zielsetzungen der Sphäre 1 sind langfristiger Natur. In der Prioritätenliste rangieren sie vor allen andern.

Die Sphäre 2 umfaßt die Problematik der Feinerschließung, d.h. der Anlage geeigneter Orientierungs-, Geh- und Fahrschneisen.

Ohne Erschließungsnetz bleibt ein Bestand gerade im frühen Stangenholzalter, wo die entscheidenden Weichen für Pflegeeffekte gestellt werden, unzugänglich.

Die Pflegeeingriffe selbst bestehen darin, daß man den verbleibenden von der Konkurrenz des ausscheidenden Bestandes befreit; zum letzteren gehört auch das Holz, das auf den Schneisen direkt anfällt.

Diese Wechselbeziehungen bewirken, daß die Sphäre 2 sowohl den verbleibenden als auch den ausscheidenden Bestand angeht. Ihre Zielsetzungen sind mittel bis kurzfristig, denn man kann unterstellen, daß eine heute angelegte Feinerschließung spätestens in 2 bis 3 Jahrzehnten, großenteils aber auch schon mit einem einzigen Pflegeeingriff ihre Funktionen erfüllt hat.

Die Sphäre 3 betrifft die technische Ausführung der vorgesehenen Durchforstungsmaßnahmen.

Hier verfolgen wir das Ziel, den ausscheidenden Bestand mit Hilfe ökonomisch optimaler Arbeitsverfahren und ggf. Sortierungs modali täten zu ernten oder doch abzutöten.

Die Optimierungsüberlegungen, die man dafür anstellt, müssen in jedem Fall halt machen vor den langfristigen und mittelfristigen Schranken, die durch die Ziele der Sphären 1 und 2 gesetzt sind.

Die Übersichten 1–3 (Tabelle 12.1) zeigen nun den Versuch, die vorgenannten Grundsätze des Durchforstens in abgestimmter Sequenz vom jungen Stangenholz bis zum älteren Pflegebestand in konkrete Vorschläge umzusetzen. Die Darstellung beschränkt sich auf "befahrbare Lagen", worunter die Ebene und Hänge bis 40% Neigung verstanden werden. Sie beschränkt sich ferner auf die Arbeitsphasen im Bestand.

Die Übersichten sind so eingeteilt, daß die lang- und mittelfristigen Funktionen der Durchforstung die waagerechte Gliederung liefern, während die Haupteinteilung in der Senkrechten nach der kurzfristigen ökonomischen Überlegung getroffen wurde, ob das Aufarbeiten des ausscheidenden Bestandes mehr einbringt als kostet (Kategorie A) oder ob es defizitär ist (Kategorie B). Bei Kategorie B wird für die Entscheidungsbildung noch weiter differenziert, ob Käferbefall droht oder nicht.

Befassen wir uns zunächst mit Übersicht 1, Kategorie A:

Die Bestandeserschließung geschieht hier durch 4–5 m breite Gassen, die u.a. zum Befahren mit Großmaschinen geeignet sind.

Der Abstand 20 m von Gassenmitte zu Gassenmitte erscheint forstschutztechnisch und ertragskundlich verantwortbar, sofern keine besondere Schneedruck- oder Sturmdisposition vorliegt. – Die verwertbare Gassendurchforstungsmasse beträgt 25–35 EFm oR je ha.

Um die Gassen rationell herstellen zu können, entwickeln wir zur Zeit eine Holzerntemaschine. Auftraggeber ist die nordrhein-westfälische Landesforstverwaltung, bei der ich mich für ihre Hilfe und Aufgeschlossenheit zu bedanken habe. Die Konstruktion erfolgt in Zusammenarbeit zwischen dem Institut für Waldarbeit und Forstmaschinenkunde

*Paper presented by J. Stratmann

114

TABELLE 12.1—*fort.*

Übersicht 1		Optimale Sequenz der Fichtendurchforstung			Stand 1974
Funktionen des Durchforstungseingriffs	Bestandesbehandlung	Jüngere Stangenhölzer (20–35 Jahre) Verfahrensmerkmale	Vorrat: 250 VFm mR/ha Sortimente in der Rückeg.	keine Käfergefahr	Käfergefahr
	Kategorie A Σ (Holzerlös – Holzerntekosten) $\geqq$ 0	Für den ausscheidenden Bestand gilt ggf.		*Kategorie B* Σ (Holzerlös-H. erntek.)<0	
1	2	3	4	5	6
Erschliessung	*Gassendurchforstung* Gassenbreite 4–5 m; Gassenabstand (von Mitte zu Mitte): ca. 20 m Gefällte Masse/ha: 15–20 % des Vorrats=30–40 EFm oR; Verwertete Masse/ha: 25–35 EFm oR.	Holzerntemaschine "Olpe". Fällen, Entasten, Abzopfen, wahlweise Einschneiden in 2m-Längen, Sammeln, Ablegen. 1 Mann-Arbeit.	Rohschäfte in fallenden Längen bis 15 m oder wahlweise Mischsortiment IN+IF 2 m lg.	*Gassenherstellung* durch Planierraupe mit Spezialaufbau; Umdrücken u. Liegenlassen der auf den Gassen stockenden Bestandesglieder. Gassenbreite und Gassenabstand wie bei Spalte 2.	Reihendurchforstung;
Standraumerweiterung für den verbleibenden Bestand	*Auslesedurchforstung in den Zwischenstreifen* a. Nach den Vorschlägen von ABETZ und KRAMER werden die Zukunftsstämme ausgewählt. b. Die Bestandesglieder, die für die Z-Stämme in den nächsten 10 Jahren lästig zu werden drohen, werden entnommen. c. Der Nebenbestand, der nicht kostendeckend aufarbeitbar ist, aber die Z-Stämme nicht belästigt, bleibt unbehandelt stehen.	1 Mann-Motorsäge, Axt, Ablängstock oder Rikleå-Band, Packhaken; Ausformen der 2 m-Längen am Stock; Vorliefern von Hand (Rückestufe nach HET: 1 oder 2); Aufsetzen in Rauhbeugen in der Rückegasse.	Standardlängen 2 m; IN und IF getrennt, oder nur IN, oder IN+IF als Mischsortiment.	*In den Zwischenstreifen* Bestandesbehandlung im Prinzip wie bei Spalte 2, jedoch werden die Bestandesglieder nach b. nicht ausgehauen, sondern durch Applizierung von Pflegepatronen abgetötet.	Entnahme jeder dritten oder vierten Reihe
Qualitätspflege für den verbleibenden Bestand	Gefällte Masse/ha zu b: 35 EFm oR Verwertete Masse/ha: 30 EFm oR	1 Mann-Arbeit in aufgelösten kleineren oder größeren Rotten.			

TABELLE 12.1—*fort.*

Optimale Sequenz der Fichtendurchforstung   Stand 1974

Mittelalte Stangenhölzer (35–50 Jahre)   Vorrat: 350 VFm mR/ha

Übersicht 2

	Kategorie A			Kategorie B	
	Für den ausscheidenden Bestand gilt ggf.				
	Σ (Holzerlös – Holzerntekosten) $\geqq 0$			Σ (Holzerlös–H. erntek.) <0	
Funktionen des Durchforstungseingriffs	Bestandesbehandlung	Verfahrensmerkmale	Sortimente in der Rückeg.	keine Käfergefahr	Käfergefahr
1	2	3	4	5	6
Erschliessung	*Gassendurchforstung* Gassenbreite: 4–5 m; Gassenabstand (von Mitte zu Mitte): ca. 25–30 m Gefällte Masse/ha: 10–15% des Vorrats =40 EFm oR Verwertete Masse/ha: 35 EFm oR	Holzerntemaschine "Olpe" Fällen, Entasten, Abzopfen, wahlweise Einschneiden in 2m-Längen, Sammeln, Ablegen. 1 Mann-Arbeit	Rohschäfte in fallenden Längen oder wahlweise Mischsortiment IN+IF 2 m lg.	*Gassenherstellung* durch Planierraupe mit Spezialaufbau; Umdrücken u. Liegenlassen der auf den Gassen stockenden Bestandesglieder. Gassenbreite und Gassenabstand wie bei Spalte 2.	
Standraumerweiterung für den verbleibenden Bestand	*Auslesedurchforstung in den Zwischenstreifen* a. Nach den Vorschlägen von ABETZ u. KRAMER werden die Zukunftsstämme ausgewählt. b. Die Bestandesglieder, die für die Z-Stämme in den nächsten 10 Jahren lästig zu werden drohen, werden entnommen. c. Der Nebenbestand, der nicht kostendeckend aufarbeitbar ist, aber die Z-Stämme nicht belästigt, bleibt unbehandelt stehen.	1 Mann-Motorsäge, Axt, Ablängstock, Packhaken, Rikleä-Band, STE-Hammer, Kleinseilwinde. Aushaltung mit Rinde; Langhölzer ab Kl. 2a werden am Stock entastet, vermessen, numeriert und mittels Kleinseilwinde vorgerückt (Alternative: Aushaltung als entastete Rohschäfte); die schwächeren entnommenen Bäume werden am Stock auf 2m-Längen eingeschnitten und manuell vorgeliefert oder von Fall zu Fall auch mit Kleinseilwinde als entastete Rohschäfte zur Rückegasse vorgerückt und dort ggf. auf 2m-Standardlängen eingeschnitten. 1 Mann-Arbeit in aufgelösten kleineren oder größeren Rotten.	Schwache Langhölzer oder Rohschäfte. Wenn keine Rohschaftsaushaltung, dann im schwächeren Bereich Standardlängen 2 m.	*In den Zwischenstreifen* Bestandesbehandlung im Prinzip wie bei Spalte 2, jedoch werden die Bestandesglieder nach b. nicht ausgehauen, sondern durch Applizierung von Pflegepatronen abgetötet.	wie Spalte 3
Qualitätspflege für den verbleibenden Bestand	Gefällte Masse/ha zu b: 40 EFm oR Verwertete Masse/ha: 35 EFm oR				

TABELLE 12.1—*fort.*

Übersicht 3	Optimale Sequenz der Fichtendurchforstung				Stand 1974
Funktionen des Durchforstungseingriffs	Altere Stangenhölzer und Baumhölzer (50–80 Jahre)				Vorrat: 450 VFm mR/ha
	Kategorie A Für den ausscheidenden Bestand gilt ggf. Σ (Holzerlös – Holzerntekosten) ≧ 0			*Kategorie B* Σ (Holzerlös–H. erntek.) < 0	
	Bestandesbehandlung	Verfahrensmerkmale	Sortimente in der Rückeg.	keine Käfergefahr	Käfergefahr
1	2	3	4	5	6
Erschliessung	*Herstellung von Rückegassen* durch Entnahme einzelner Stämme von Fall zu Fall Verwertete Masse/ha = 15 EFm oR	1. *Durchgang:* Ausscheidende Bäume mit BHD>20–25 cm: Stehendentastung und -entrindung. 2 Mann, 5 SERIAS, 1 Trackster. 2. *Durchgang:* 1 Mann-Motorsäge, Axt, Rikleå-Band oder Ablängstock, STE-Hammer, evtl. Kleinseilwinde.	Langholz oR;		
Standraumerweiterung für den verbleibenden Bestand	*Selektive Durchforstung* zur Begünstigung der Z-Stämme	Fällen, Abzopfen, Vermessen, Numerieren der SERIAS-Stämme. Fällen, Entasten, Abzopfen, (Vermessen) der ausscheidenden Bestandesglieder mit BHD<20–25 cm.	Langholz mR; evtl. Rohschäfte;	Bedränger der Z-Stämme werden durch Applizierung von Pflegepatronen abgetötet.	wie Spalte 3
Qualitätspflege für den verbleibenden Bestand	Verwertete Masse/ha = 50 EFm oR	Bei BHD<20–25 cm evtl. 2 m-Aushaltung am Stock und Vorliefern von Hand; evtl. auch Vorrücken der Rohschäfte mit Kleinseilwinde u. Einschneiden auf 2m-Längen an der Rückegasse. 1 Mann-Arbeit in aufgelösten kleineren oder größeren Rotten.	evtl. 2 m – Standardlängen		

der Universität Göttingen und einigen Industriefirmen.

Die Maschine wird von einem Mann bedient. Sie kann fällen, entasten, abzopfen und im Endstadium Rohschäfte bis 15 m Länge oder wahlweise 2 m Standardlängen einschneiden, sammeln und ablegen.

Die Forderungen der Boden- und Bestandespfleglichkeit haben die Eigenschaften unseres Vollernters stark beeinflußt; ich darf dies kurz begründen:

1. Das Astreisig und die Kronenenden werden beim Entastungsprozeß vor dem Fahrzeug ausgebreitet. Es entsteht also auf der Rückegasse ein Teppich, der die Wurzeln der Randbäume beim Überfahren schützt.

2. Die lang ausgehaltenen Hölzer laufen nach dem Entasten hinter die Maschine in die freie Gasse hinein. Dadurch wollen wir Rindenverletzungen an den Wurzelanläufen und Erdstücken der Randstämme vorbeugen.

3. Die Maschine besitzt ein Raupenfahrwerk. Dieses gewährleistet

   (a) geringen Bodendruck und also i.V. mit der Reisigauflage besonders gute Wurzelschonung

   (b) eine relativ geringe Höhe des Gesamtfahrzeugs, so daß die Aufbauten bei Bodenunebenheiten und entsprechenden Kippbewegungen die Stämme und Kronen der Randbäume möglichst wenig beschädigen.

Weitere Vorteile hat das Kettenfahrzeug durch seine Geländegängigkeit und den niedrigen Schwerpunkt, der Abstützungen entbehrlich macht. Gewisse Schwierigkeiten verursacht das Umsetzen über größere Distanzen und insbesondere öffentliche Straßen. Man darf diesen Gesichtspunkt aber nicht überbewerten. Der Rationalisierungseffekt eines Vollernters beruht nämlich auf der Integration mehrerer Bearbeitungsgänge und gar nicht so sehr auf hohen Mengenleistungen; wir können einen Flächenverzehr von 1–1,5 ha pro Tag unterstellen und brauchen also nicht zu befürchten, vom Umsetzen organisatorisch erdrückt zu werden, selbst wenn man Tieflader benötigt. Abgesehen davon ist es natürlich in der Raupengestaltung auch noch nicht aller Tage Abend.

Die maschinelle Vollernte spielt sich allein au der Gassenfläche ab. Zu dünne Bäumchen werden umgedrückt und bleiben liegen. Seitliche Eingriffe entfallen, denn die Such- und Schwenkbewegungen des Fällkrans würden dabei zu lange dauern und zu viel kosten. Das haben schon die Simulationen mit unserem ersten Funktionsmodell gezeigt.

Auf den Streifen zwischen den Gassen erscheinen selektive Entnahmen mit konventioneller Ausformung von 2 m – Standardlängen am Stock und manuellem Vorliefern optimal. Die verwertbare Erntemasse mag 30 EFm oR je ha betragen. Zu dünne, nicht kostendeckend nutzbare Bäumchen bleiben auf den Zwischenstreifen unbehandelt stehen und sterben allmählich von selbst ab. Bis dahin bremsen sie die stärkeren Bäume beim Ausschwingen in der Windbewegung und vermindern so die Sturmwurfgefahr. – Ein besonderer Vorteil der Kurzholz-Methode ist ihr bestandesschonender Arbeitsablauf. Er gestattet es, jüngere Stangenhölzer auch im Sommer zu durchforsten, was die betriebliche Disposition außerordentlich erleichtert.

Für Gassen und Streifen zusammen werden rund 60 EFm oR je ha in einem Durchgang entnommen. Diese Masse bedeutet etwa ein Viertel des Vorrats und liegt nach Ansicht kompetenter Ertragskundler noch im Unbedenklichkeitsrahmen; andererseits bildet sie aber für die Auslastung der beteiligten Großmaschinen auch bereits eine günstige Größenordnung.

In der Übersicht fehlt die Variante, daß die Gasse neben der Erschließung auch die Standraumerweiterung für den verbleibenden Bestand voll bewerkstelligt. Diese Zielkombination würde voraussetzen, daß man die Gassenabstände – vom Mitte zu Mitte – auf etwa 10 bis 12 m verkürzt. So vorzugehen, käme zwar der Wirtschaftlichkeit unseres Vollernters zugute und erscheint mir in Jungdurchforstungen auch waldbaulich durchaus denkbar, es fehlen aber ausreichende Erfahrungen, um dazu heute schon ein fundiertes Urteil abgeben zu können. – Wir haben allerdings im Raum Göttingen zusammen mit der Niedersächsischen Forstlichen Versuchsanstalt derartige Versuchsflächen eingerichtet, um die notwendigen Langzeitbeobachtungen anzustellen.

Werfen wir nun einen Blick auf die *Kategorie B*, die als kurzfristiges Ziel eine Verlustminimierung beim momentanen Durchforstungseingriff verfolgt.

Besteht keine Käfergefahr, so wird man hier nach dem erfolgreichen Vorgang, den Prof. KRAMER im Forstamt Hardegsen geschaffen hat, die Gassen mit Hilfe schwerer Raupen herstellen, die das aufstockende Holz einfach niederwalzen.–In den Zwischenstreifen gilt es, die Bedränger der Z-Stämme möglichst billig auszuschalten, was zweckmäßigerweise mit der von Dr. STERZIK entwickelten Pflegepatrone geschieht. Sie einzuschlagen, dauert kaum länger als das Anbringen eines Schalms. Die Maßnahme läßt sich also im gleichen Zuge mit der Z-Stamm-Auswahl durch den Betriebsbeamten selbst erledigen. – Übrigens schließen sich mechanische Eingriffe und Pflegepatrone nicht aus, sondern man kann selbstverständlich beide Techniken in ein und demselben Bestand nach dieser oder jener

Überlegung verknüpfen. Darin sehe ich sogar künftig einen Haupteffekt der Patrone.

In Sp. 6 der Übersicht 1 tritt die Reihendurchforstung auf. Sie ist den bisher besprochenen Alternativen im allgemeinen technisch und wirtschaftlich unterlegen. Andererseits gibt es aber doch spezifische Zielsetzungen, die man durch reihenweise Entnahmen optimal verwirklichen kann, so zum Beispiel, wenn mit geringstmöglichem Verwaltungsaufwand Selbstwerber eingesetzt werden sollen oder wenn es unter Verzicht auf eine Holzverwertung darum geht, jüngere Stangenhölzer zu erschließen, zur Wuchsraumerweiterung aufzulockern und ggf. die entnommen Bäume aus Forstschutzgründen außerhalb des Bestandes zu verbrennen.

Damit komme ich zu *Ubersicht 2*, also zu den Durchforstungsmaßnahmen im Bestandesalter 35 bis 50.

Auch hier dient unser Vollernter, wenn noch kein Erschließungsnetz vorhanden ist, zur Herstellung der Gassen, nur muß man deren Abstände jetzt wegen der höheren Bäume und damit auch höheren Sturmgefahr etwas erweitern.

Die Sortimentierung wird mit zunehmendem Bestandesalter zu größeren Längen tendieren. Eine Generalempfehlung ist aber nicht möglich. Die konkrete Sortierentscheidung müssen die Preis-Kosten-Relationen und die örtlichen Aspekte der Marktpflege bringen, die im Zeitpunkt des Hiebs gelten.

Um das Vorrücken langer Schwachhölzer zu erleichtern, dienen tragbare oder schleppermontierte Kleinseilwinden mit Funkfernsteuerung. Sie sind bei guter Arbeitsorganisation einigermaßen wirtschaftlich und arbeiten, da der Holzhauer den laufenden Stamm begleitet, recht bestandesschonend.

Für Reihendurchforstungen ist es im Bestandes-Alter 35–50 meist zu spät. Man wird also, wenn Käfergefahr droht, trotz momentan erhöhter Verluste nicht umhin können, den Durchforstungseingriff rein mechanisch zu gestalten und das anfallende Holz auch aufzuarbeiten.

Den dritten Sektor des Durchforstungsbereichs – dem die *Übersicht 3* entspricht – bilden die älteren Stangenhölzer und Baumhölzer zwischen 50 und 80 Jahren. Als günstigste Erntetechnik können wir hier das SERIAS-System bezeichnen, jedenfalls für Bäume über BHD 25. Verfahrens- und Kostendetails sind in der Fachliteratur ausführlich beschrieben. – Unterhalb BHD 25 werden am besten unentrindete Langhölzer oder Rohschäfte ausgehalten, evtl. auch Industrieholz 2 m lang. Fichtenbestände zwischen 50 und 80 Jahren stehen im allgemeinen schon so locker, daß Rückegassen dort, wo sie fehlen, leicht durch den Auszug relativ weniger Stämme freigehauen werden können. Der

weit überwiegende Anteil der Erntemasse entfällt auf selektive Entnahmen zugunsten der Zukunftsbäume. – Hinsichtlich der Reihendurchforstung gilt das, was ich bereits zu Übersicht 2 ausgeführt habe.

Die Übersichten 1–3 sind damit zu Ende besprochen.

Eiene Diskussion der Durchforstungsprobleme bliebe jedoch allzu unvollständig, wenn nicht zumindest noch zwei Fragenkreise mit angerissen würden, nämlich als Kontaktpunkt zur Zielsphäre 1 die Wertästung und als Kontaktpunkt zu den Zielsphären 2 und 3 das Rücken.

Astreines Fichtenstarkholz liefert nach einschlägigen Erfahrungen die 1,5 bis 2 fachen Verkaufserlöse der Massenware. Alle Prognosen deuten darauf hin, daß diese Relation in Zukunft eher weiter als enger wird. – Wir sollten deshalb die starken Auslesedurchforstungen, wie sie den Übersichten 1–3 entsprechen, und bei denen man ja sowieso die Z-Stämme sehr gewissenhaft auswählen muß, künftig vermehrt mit Wertästungen koppeln. Sie in Angriff zu nehmen, empfiehlt sich bei der Fichte, wenn die Brusthöhendurchmesser der Z-Stämme 10 bis 15 cm erreicht haben.

Die Arbeitstechnik ist für Hochästungen gut gelöst, denn dafür gibt es die SACHS-Klettersäge KS 31; arbeitstechnisch eher problematisch erscheinen noch die untersten 5–6 m am Stamm, da hier mit hohen ergonomischen Belastungen manuell geästet wird, und die Produktivität vergleichsweise gering ist. – Wir hoffen jedoch, der Praxis in Bälde ein geeignetes Maschinenwerkzeug für Ästungshöhen bis 5 m vorstellen zu können.

Nun zum Rückeproblem:

Das Rücken schließt sich an die Bereitstellungsstadien des Rohholzes an, mit denen die Übersichten 1–3 enden. Es bildet eine untrennbare Ergänzung zu den dort aufgezeigten Arbeitsverfahren und kann weder unter dem Aspekt der Boden- und Bestandesschonung, noch bei kurzfristigen Wirtschaftlichkeitsüberlegungen unbeachtet bleiben.

Kurzholz rücken wir aus Durchforstungsbeständen am besten mit Forwardern oder Kranrückezügen heraus. Sie befördern 10–15 Rm in einer Fuhre. Das ergibt in Verbindung mit dem erheblichen Eigengewicht besonders höhe Bodendrucke, die auf wenig tragfähigen Böden zum Einbrechen führen können. Andererseits ist die große Ladekapazität aber auch wieder ein Vorteil, denn sie reduziert den Schlupf und bewirkt, daß jede Rückegasse meist nur ein Mal mit Last befahren werden muß.

Abgesehen davon pflegen in den Rückegassen, besonders bei Ersteingriffen, beachtliche Reisigmengen aufzuliegen, die eine ausgezeichnete Schutz- und Trageschicht liefern.

Die Forwarder und Kranrückezüge sind einmannbedient. Bei guter Auslastung rücken sie im Schwachholzbereich konkurrenzlos billig. Technisch und organisatorisch ist ihr Einsatz in Verbindung mit der 2 m – Aushaltung bestens erprobt und zwar nicht nur in Schweden als Standardverfahren, sondern auch in der Bundesrepublik. Ich erwähne die richtungsweisenden Bemühungen des Gräflich Königsegg'schen Forstamts Königseggwald schon zu Beginn der 60er Jahre und 10 Jahre später den Großversuch des Instituts für Waldarbeit und Forstmaschinenkunde in der Kiefer der Lüneburger Heide.

Lange Hölzer rücken wir gewöhnlich mit Seilwindenschleppern. Sie müssen jede Rückegasse mehrfach befahren, da ihre Lasten pro Fahrt bei kleinen Stückmassen einen Festmeter selten übersteigen, wohl aber oft darunter liegen. Hängt man wesentlich größere Mengen an, so erhöhen sich durch das Auseinanderfächern der Last die Schäden an den stehenden Stämmen progressiv, wie überhaupt die Schadwirkungen des Langrückens für den verbleibenden Bestand die des Kurzrückens eindeutig übertreffen. Ich verweise dazu auf die Untersuchungen, die BACKHAUS in der Buche angestellt hat. Aufgrund dieser Zusammenhänge kommt das Rücken mit Seilwinden-Schleppern je Masseneinheit im Schwachholz sehr viel teurer als das Rücken mit Forwardern. Man kann also die Vergleichskostenvorteile, die die Langaushaltung am Stock gegenüber dem Kurzholz dank geringerer Arbeiterzeiten erbringt, leicht beim Rücken sowie beim späteren Sortieren und Einschneiden oder – wenn man

Rohschäfte verkauft – auch beim Holzpreis wieder verlieren.

Über die Leistungsmöglichkeiten und Kosten höher mechanisierter Schleifrückefahrzeuge wie Klemmbank- oder Grapple-Skidder wissen wir unter Verhältnissen, die auf unsere Durchforstungen passen, noch nicht viel. Es wird eine wichtige Aufgabe der näheren Zukunft sein, für diese Technologien brauchbare Indizes zu erarbeiten.

Damit komme ich zum Schluß meiner Ausführungen. Ihr Zweck war, die wesentlichen Grundsätze aufzuzeigen, die uns bei unseren Versuchen geleitet haben. Vor allem ging es mir darum, zu verdeutlichen, daß hier nicht nur punktuell vorgegangen wurde, sondern im Rahmen eines abgestimmten technischen Konzepts, das sich über den Gesamtbereich der Fichtendurchforstung erstreckt und speziell auf die Mechanisierung der Holzerntearbeiten im Bestand abzielt. Diese Blickrichtung ist insofern einigermaßen originell, als man sie zugunsten der Propaganda für Holzhöfe und für mobile Mechanisierungslösungen an Waldstraßen und Aufarbeitungsplätzen jedenfalls in der Bundesrepublik Deutschland allzulang vernachlässigt hat.

Mit dem Vollernter am Anfang, dem SERIAS-System am Ende und der Pflegepatrone als ultima ratio der Durchforstungsphase besitzen wir nun ein Gerüst, das selbstverständlich im einzelnen fortwährend mit aktuellen Verfahrensbausteinen gefüllt und auch nach außen ergänzt werden muß, das aber an sich schon ohne Zweifel eine neue Epoche unserer Durchforstungstechnik verkörpert.

LITERATUR

ABETZ, P. Zur Bestandesbegründung und Jung-bestandspflege in Fichte. *Der Forst- und Holzwirt* 1966, S. 77–88.

ABETZ, P. Der Wald und die Forsttechnik. *Der Forst- und Holzwirt* Nr. 15/1973.

BACKHAUS, G. Leistungs- und Kostenvergleich zwischen Pferd, Radiotir und Drabant beim Vorrücken von Laubindustrieholz in langer Form. *Holz-Zentralblatt* Nr. 69/1970.

BACKHAUS, G. Rationelle Schwachholzbringung und Bestandespfleglichkeit – ein Gegensatz? *Forsttechn. Informationen* Nr. 3/1972.

HÄBERLE, S. u. RAUSCH, E. Das Rücken schwacher Langhölzer mit Schlepper und funkferngesteuerter Kleinseilwinde. *Forsttechn. Informationen* Nr. 4/1970.

HÄBERLE, S. Mechanisierte Kiefernschwachholzernte in der Lüneburger Heide – Modell und Realität – (Vortrag anläßl. d. Forstl. Hochschulwoche 1971 in Göttingen). *Forsttechn. Informationen* Nr. 10/1971.

HÄBERLE, S. Die Stehendbearbeitung von Durchforstungshölzern der Fichte im Systemvergleich. *Allgem. Forstzeitschrift* Nr. 28/1973.

HÄBERLE, S. Wie bietet sich das SERIAS-System bei differenzierterer Betrachtung dar? *Allgem. Forstzeitschrift* Nr. 5/1974

HÄBERLE, S. Ist die Stehendentastung und -entrindung eine wirtschaftliche Alternative zur Werksentrindung? *Holz-Zentralblatt* vom 6.2.1974.

HÖFLE, H. H. *Holzaufarbeitung mit stationären Einrichtungen.* Vortrag anläßlich der Fachtagung INTERFORST 1974 in München.

HOHENLOHE-WALDENBURG, KARL PRINZ ZU u. BÜRGMANN, P. Das Königseggwalder Holzernte-Verfahren und seine Auswirkungen auf Masse, Leistung und Ertrag. *Allgem. Forstzeitschrift* Nr 18/1966.

KRAMER, H. u. KEUFFEL, W. Gassendurchforstung. *Allgem. Forstzeitschrift* Nr 7/1974.

MALMBERG, C. E. *Holzaufarbeitung mit mobilen Einrichtungen.* Vortrag anläßlich der Fachtagung INTERFORST 1974 in München.

STERZIK, H. K. Zur Anwendung der drahtlosen Fernsteuerung bei der Holzbringung. *Forsttechn. Informationen* Nr 2/1971.

STERZIK, H. K. Systeme der Hochmechanisierung bei der Schwachholzernte. (Vortrag anläßlich der Forstl. Hochschulwoche 1971 in Göttingen). *Forsttechn. Informationen* Nr 10/1971.

STERZIK, H. K. Zur mechanisierten Aufbereitung des Rohholzes am Fällort. *Holz-Zentralblatt* vom 14.6.1974.

DISCUSSION

Busby: You suggest in the final paragraph of your summary (Page 9) that "for the long term aim in a cultivated forest demands thinning operations independent of the price/cost situation operating at that time". I wonder how you can justify this in terms of allocation of resources. You seem to be avoiding economics altogether.

Stratmann: We regard a thinning which costs us more than the revenue we obtain from it as an investment. Of course, we have to consider the whole rotation and we are concerned with increasing the revenue obtained from the final crop.

Busby: If the cost of removing these thinnings is, in terms of net present value, greater than the extra revenue from your felling surely this is not a correct allocation of your resources.

Stratmann: I would agree with you if we considered compound interest but our principle is to maximise the annual forest rent. We use the whole forest as a production unit and compare our costs and revenues for a single year.

Busby: I think nonetheless that there is a cost of capital in the sense that there are alternative uses which you can make of capital and therefore you must, in fact, use compound interest.

Kramer: I think the question you are asking is one of forest policy. In Germany and Austria the method of financial appraisal differs from those in certain other countries.

Rowan: I think this particular question is extremely difficult to answer. There are many different attitudes adopted by different countries according to whether they have got the forest given to them by God in the first instance or whether, as in Britain, we have to help the Good Lord along.

Fries: Regarding machines which climb, delimb and debark, it is my impression that the time is past for such machines in view of the fact that they must be carried from tree to tree.

Stratmann: We are trying at the moment to use a small tractor for carrying the machines from tree to tree because undoubtedly the main drawback of these machines is that they have to be transported in the stand by hand.

THINNING; THE STATE OF THE ART IN THE PACIFIC NORTHWEST

by B. D. E. AULERICH

Oregon State University, Corvallis, Oregon, USA

Commercial thinning in Douglas-fir (*Pseudotsuga menziesii*) is finally coming into its own in the Pacific Northwest (Oregon, Washington, and British Columbia). This type of intensive forest management has been a long time in coming and is welcomed by both forester and logger. But there are some major obstacles to overcome before commercial thinning is really a viable part of the total wood supply system.

The availability of stands in need of thinning is abundant as is the market for these thinnings. In western Washington and Oregon there are nearly 3·3 million acres (1·3 million hectares) of Douglas-fir forests between 20 and 70 years old. The estimated volume is 38 billion board feet (269 million cubic metres). The activities necessary to bridge the gap between stand and mill will be the subject of this paper. This area of operation is the major problem facing the industry. How do we economically harvest stands which are located on steep ground, in high rainfall areas, and with woods workers who are trained to operate large, expensive equipment to log large old-growth timber.

State of the Art

Before we delve very far into the equipment and techniques used let us look at how thinning is viewed by the average logger in the Northwestern United States. In a survey of thinning operations in Oregon and Washington conducted in the spring of 1973, 11 percent of the operators who were thinning were doing so in stands more than 100 years old and 38 percent were operating in stands in excess of 50 years of age (2). For instance, using a Site Class III stand classification, 11 percent of the operators were "thinning" stands that averaged in excess of 13,270 cubic feet per acre (926 cubic metres per hectare) and 38 percent were thinning stands containing 7,050 cubic feet per acre (492 cubic metres per hectare). Can this really be called thinning? The attitude, in short, has been one which considers thinning as a means of capturing mortality or preparing the stand for final harvest rather than stimulating growth in young stands. In truth much of the harvest is really a partial cut.

Let us take a brief look at some of the equipment being used to thin these stands. Because of the steep topography, fragile soils and regulation of logging practices found in our region, cable systems are used extensively (33 percent). However, ground-based systems such as crawler tractors and rubber-tyred skidders still accounted for 62 percent of the equipment used. Five percent of the operations used other systems such as horses or helicopters.

If we focus our attention on the cable systems we find that 28% of the operators use large tower systems or loaders commonly used for harvesting old-growth timber. Another 31 percent used machines classed as medium in size but would be considered "large" in most parts of the world. A machine classified as medium-sized would have a 200–300 horsepower engine with a 50 to 60 foot (approximately 15 to 20 metres) tower and cost between $80,000–$120,000 or, in the case of an interlock system, $160,000.

The study further showed that 41 percent were using cable systems that can be considered smallwood harvesting machines. These include the Skagit S.J. series (SJ4, SJ5, and SJ8) which still have ratings of 300+ horsepower. Also included in this group are the Urus (90 hp) and the Schield-Bantam T-350 (100 hp).

This survey illustrates very clearly that the Western United States is not being flooded with cable equipment economically capable of harvesting smallwood (under 100 b.f. or 0·7 cubic metres). Most of the equipment in use is obsolete mobile-loaders with short distance capabilities (up to 600 feet or 200 metres) or units of foreign manufacture designed for use under other conditions.

Why all the big equipment for such little logs? There are several reasons presented by loggers, all of which may be valid. One reason can be traced to a landowner policy of requiring all old-growth trees left from former operations be taken along with the thinnings. Consequently, the occasional 4-foot "hooter" left from previous logging must now be taken. Either it has value now that it never had before or it is to be removed to "clean up" the stand. As a result, the thinning operator must gear his equipment to enable him to yard this occasional large log rather than scale his operation to the smaller stems which may comprise 95 to 99% of the stand. This is a management problem that takes some careful analysis in order to determine whether or not scattered old-growth should be removed.

A key reason that large equipment is used for thinning is that nothing else is presently available. No major American logging equipment company is currently manufacturing a cable yarder designed especially for thinning under our forest conditions. Operators, therefore, must rely on obsolete, expensive systems for removal of the thinnings. Such equipment is not appropriate for use on the steeper slopes and fragile soils which cover a large part of our thinnable stands.

Since most of the thinning is presently being done with ground-based equipment some discussion is in order. These systems are being criticized primarily because of excessive soil compaction that may retard stand growth rate and also residual stand damage. Extensive research is being conducted on the soil problem by both private and public agencies. Dr. Henry Froehlich, of our staff, is involved in one of these projects. Some public agencies now prohibit the use of ground equipment for harvesting on slopes greater than 20%. As thinning becomes more extensive in the Pacific Northwest, the proportion of the thinning activity carried out by ground equipment will drop.

Much of the logging and nearly all of the access road construction is done by blade-equipped crawler tractors. Therefore, it is not surprising that many small operators have only tractors in their machinery inventory. These independent operators or contract loggers are also the primary source of thinning contracts in the region.

Our survey revealed that of 138 operators using ground-based units, 34% used crawler tractors only and 23% used rubber-tyred skidders exclusively, but the majority, 43%, used a combination of the two for thinning.

All sizes of crawler tractors are being used for thinning, but large machines are most common. Large machines, 125 to 180 flywheel horsepower class, are used primarily because they are available from other operations. The most common crawler being used was the Caterpillar D-6.

Rubber-tyred skidder use is increasing, primarily due to the lower initial investment and also due to the fact that smaller logs make the units more economical than cable systems (9). Skid distance is a large factor and the speed of the skidder can be an advantage in long skid situations.

New types of track laying machines are coming into the industry primarily because of the interest of ground pressure influence on soil compaction. The Washington Iron Works "Tracmac", FMC logging tractor, and the Foremost soft-tracked log skidder are all designed to be all-terrain, low ground pressure machines. More research and development in smaller models will be required before these machines will be widely used in thinning operations.

Research Activities on Thinning Systems

Several different thinning operations have been monitored over the past two years by the Forest Engineering department at Oregon State University. The purpose has been to identify and measure the factors that influence the production rates of different thinning systems. Heretofore information of this sort was minimal.

A study in 35-year old Douglas fir using a Schield-Bantam skyline yarder was conducted in the fall of 1972 (1). The results of this study were reported at the IUFRO meeting in Vancouver, B.C. in August 1973 and are to be printed in the proceedings of that meeting (2).

The objective of that study was to compare skyline and tractor operations according to cost, production, and soil and stand damage. As was expected, skylining was more expensive and resulted in more slash remaining on the site. It also produced less soil compaction and fewer serious wounds to residual trees. The higher costs were due primarily to the higher capital investment in equipment and larger crew requirements on the skyline. On gentle slopes (20%), the tractor outproduced the skyline but on steeper slopes (40%) the output was reversed. The primary factors that influenced skyline production were distance out on the skyline and lateral distance from the skyline. The production of both systems was influenced by thinning intensity, logs per turn, and slope (4).

Another study conducted by the Forest Engineering Department was an analysis of the production of a low investment, "homemade" yarder. This yarder is operating on private land in Western Oregon. The yarder was powered by a 352 Ford V8 gasoline engine with a Fordamatic transmission. The drum assembly was a Skagit BU-30. Regressions developed from time studies showed lateral distance and slope as the most significant variable in predicting turn time (7). Total production costs and residual stand damage have not been analysed at this writing.

The major difference between this operation and the Schield-Bantam operation described above is that the skyline roads were not precut for the "homemade" yarder. Also, the machine is unable to rotate while landing the logs. This results in a swing machine being required to skid the logs away from the landing. The requirement to have another piece of equipment available for swinging is also one of the main disadvantages of the Urus system.

Decking turns on very narrow landings is a major problem in thinning our western Douglas-fir stands. Since environmental concern for soil stability will continue to reduce the size of landings, much of our work is based upon the premise that the road prism alone will be our landing in a majority of the thinning operations. Narrow landings pose special problems in the 30–40 years age class where a substantial portion of the stems removed are poles (4). Long poles make landing difficult and sorting imperative, especially when the turns include both long poles and short sawlogs. Studies are now being conducted to determine the minimum percentage of poles necessary in a stand to warrant their exclusion from a thinning operation based upon decking difficulties alone.

A carriage design with slackpulling capabilities operating from a continuous line system has been designed by Mr. Marvin Rowley, and is being tested by the Forest Engineering Department. The proto-type is large for thinnings. However, a smaller version of the design has possible application. The carriage will allow lateral yarding and remain stationary on the skyline. This feature is vital to thinning activities to minimize skyline road changes and also to keep residual stem damage down.

In my opinion, the ideal machine for thinning in the Douglas-fir forests of the Western United States would be a small, mobile, low initial investment, cable machine capable of reaching out 1,000 feet (305 metres) or more on a skyline with line speeds of 1,000–1,500 feet (305–457 metres) per minute. The system must be capable of lateral skidding from the skyline a minimum of 150 feet (46 metres). This system must be mobile enough so that it can be moved easily and set up rapidly. The carrier should be narrow enough to allow decking on the roadway beside the machine. The operator's cab should be constructed to allow the operator easy access on and off the machine. This would permit the operator to unhook the chokers. An interlock between mainline and haulback drums should be standard. And finally, the total cost should be under $50,000 to enable small contract loggers to get into the business. To this end, Prof. Lin Johnson, Mechanical Engin-eering Department, Oregon State and I are working on a conceptual yarder design that will attempt to meet these specifications. Although this concept is in the development stage we hope to have a proto-type operating in 1975.

In conclusion, the two major problems we are facing in the western United States are, first, lack of small cable yarding systems designed specifically to handle smallwood, and second, the general attitude among operators, land owners, and equipment manufacturers that only large logs harvested with large equipment and big crews are economical. We are going to have to "think small' and at the same time "think more".

REFERENCES

1. AULERICH, D. E. (1973). *Production rates and economic opportunities in thinning.* Paper presented at the Joint Meeting Project Group F 4.02, International Union of Forest Research Organizations, Vancouver, B.C. August 20–24, 1973.

2. ————. (1974). *Survey of thinning operations and equipment in western Oregon and Washington.* Unpublished data. Forest Engineering Department, Oregon State University.

3. AULERICH, D. EDWARD, AND JOHNSON, K. NORMAN. (1973). Cable thinning in young-growth Douglas-fir: A case study. In: *Management of young Douglas-fir and Western Hemlock Symposium, June 11–13, 1973.* A. B. Berg, ED. School of Forestry, Oregon State University, Corvallis. (In Press).

4. AULERICH, D. EDWARD, JOHNSON, K. NORMAN, AND FROEHLICH, HENRY. (1974). *Thinning young-growth Douglas-fir: tractors or skylines?* Forest Research Laboratory, School of Forestry, Oregon State University, Paper 954. p. 14.

5. BERG, ALAN B. (1970). Skidding with a horse. In: *Managing young Douglas-fir and Western Hemlock,* June 10–14, 1968. A. B. Berg, Ed. School of Forestry, Oregon State University, Corvallis. p. 94–96.

6. HELLAND, MARVIN L. (1970). Commercial thinning – how we do it. In: *Managing young Douglas-fir and Western Hemlock,* June 10–14, 1968. A. B. Berg, Ed. School of Forestry. Oregon State University, Corvallis. p. 114–121.

7. JONAS, WILLIAM AND STINNETT, BRENT. (1974). *Production estimates of a homemade yarder in skyline thinning operations.* Unpublished data. Forest Engineering Department, Oregon State University.

8. MCCULLEY, ROBERT D. (1970). Thinning in conifers of the Western United States. In: *Thinning and Mechanization,* IUFRO Meeting, Royal College of Forestry, Stockholm, Sweden September, 1969.

9. SCHILLINGS, PAUL L. (1969). *A technique for comparing the costs of skidding methods.* Inter. For. and Range Exper. Sta. Research Paper INT-60, p. 23.

10. SINNER, HANS-ULRICH. (1973). *Simulating skyline yarding in thinning young forests.* A paper presented at IUFRO meeting in Freiburg, Germany, October 1–5, 1973. Unpublished.

11. TESSIER, J. P. (1970). Logging techniques in thinnings today and tomorrow on the North American West Coast. In: *Thinning and Mechanization,* IUFRO Meeting, Royal College of Forestry, Stockholm, Sweden, September, 1969.

PROBLEMS OF EXTRACTION OF THINNINGS BY CABLE CRANE IN THE UNITED KINGDOM

By J. A. DRUMMOND

Forestry Commission of Great Britain

1. Introduction

In the mountainous areas of the United Kingdom where slopes exceed 50% the standard method of extraction since 1963 has been by cable crane, first in the form of high lead and later as a skyline system. (See cover picture, bottom left).

The cable cranes used at present are in the short to medium range groups. With loads of one tonne the maximum ranges are 140 m for high lead working and 450 m for skylines. Those skylines which are rated at $1\frac{1}{2}$ tonne load have a range of 350 m. Cable crane systems of these ranges and load capabilities are currently available on the British market and will cover the majority of mountain harvesting situations until 1980 when there will be a need for some longer range cranes.

2. Requirements of the Cable Crane

To work efficiently a cable crane must have:

(a) A suitable road system with spacing at from 600 to 800 m.
(b) Correct layout of the working area and racking system.
(c) Correct presentation of produce.
(d) A thinning yield sufficient to optimise the costs of erection and dismantling.
(e) A mean tree size which is large enough to permit collection of a payload in reasonable time.
(f) A small number of products (one or two) for economic handling.
(g) Good trees to act as masts and anchors.

3. Racks or Traces

Rack spacing which depends on the harvesting system employed is generally set at 25 m for manual shortwood and 40 m for manual length methods. Racks 3 m wide are set along the best extraction alignment and they seldom coincide with planting lines. Where tree rows are 1·8 m apart some 9% of the standing volume is removed when racks are at 25 m spacing, or 7% at 40 m spacing. In rack layout the rack is usually stopped 20 m short of the perimeter of the area to be thinned.

4. Thinning Yield and Average Tree Size

The use of the cable crane for extraction of thinnings is sensitive to the volume per hectare and, as with many other extraction systems, the mean size of tree being removed. Yield and mean tree size are generally both low in first thinnings or in low yield crops and it has been found that it is necessary to obtain a minimum output of 10 m³ per 100 m run of rack in order to justify economically the set-up of a cable crane. With a rack length of 300 m and a yield of 10 m³ per 100 m run of rack it has been found that the erection and dismantling of a cable crane takes 20 standard minutes per m³. If the yield is increased to 15 m³ per 100 m run of rack the time drops to 13 standard minutes per m³, a reduction of 35%. If the rack length reduces to 200 m, a common distance in first thinning, and only part of the area is thinnable, the difference between 10 m³ and 15 m³ per 100 m run of rack is again over 30% so that it clearly pays to delay thinning where yields are low or to reduce range even further to allow the use of a highlead system which is very much less sensitive to yield.

In a low yield situation one may have to delay thinning, thin more heavily than normal, or increase the rack espacement but in the last case there is a penalty in terminal time because of the increased side haul, except for tree length working in a chevron type of thinning pattern. (See Figure 14.1).

The same effect of low yield is found in areas of variable growth, and if blank or unthinnable areas are encountered the average extraction distance is increased as well as yield being further reduced. Non-selective line (geometric) thinnings are advantageous to cable crane working in that produce is concentrated in one place, but straightforward removal of one row in every three or four rows is not acceptable because of the low yield obtained from each set up of the cable crane. A pattern of non-selective thinning, which results in the removal of up to 40% of the standing volume, has been devised for cable crane extraction. It employs side racks at right angles to the main rack, but is suitable only for manual shortwood working.

Load collection in manual shortwood systems is carried out during the felling phase, but in tree length systems this is done by the chokerman. The smaller the mean tree size the greater is the load

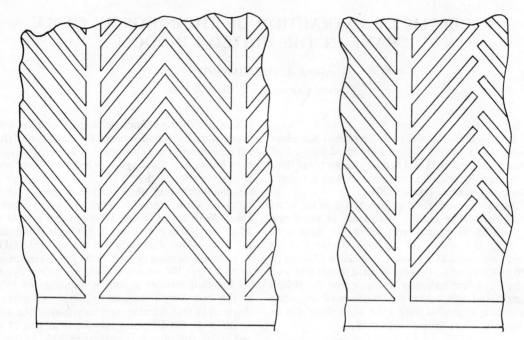

Figure 14.1   Chevron and staggered chevron patterns of line thinning.

collection time, although line thinnings can help to increase the mean tree size slightly. Anchor, support and mast trees can be a problem in first thinnings since they are often not strong enough to support a full payload and their low height means more intermediate supports for the cable.

5. Effects on Stability

Racks cut for cable crane extraction provide a possible source of windthrow, but since most of the cable crane areas are on freely drained slopes, no great difficulty has been experienced from that source except in small areas of impeded drainage. Where chevron thinning patterns have been introduced there is some evidence that the chevron junction can provide a starting point for windthrow but this can be reduced by changing to a staggered chevron pattern. (See Figure 14.1).

In cable crane extraction certain small areas are often left unthinned, for example, when high leading in a manual shortwood system only 10 m may be thinned beyond the spar tree, or with a skyline system thinning does not extend beyond the spar tree. These unthinned areas may become unstable unless dealt with on the next occasion.

6. Damage to Soil and Trees

The amount of soil damage created by cable crane extraction of thinnings is almost negligible apart from some rupture of contour drains which are normally repaired immediately after the completion of thinning operations. Rupture of the soil surface is most uncommon due to the brash mat and no problem of soil erosion has yet arisen in the United Kingdom. If future extraction systems should include the removal of whole trees to a lower landing for processing, there may be a possibility of soil disturbance and subsequent erosion in high rainfall areas in the west of the country.

Damage to trees can be a problem with a high lead system when the sap is starting to rise in the spring but good operational techniques can reduce it to a minimum. Skyline extraction systems cause little damage to rackside trees but mast and anchor trees must be protected from damage by slings, chains or guy ropes as they are required for future working. In selective thinning any damage which occurs is widely distributed whereas mechanical systems confine it to main extraction racks with most damage being caused to the exit trees.

7. Equipment and Outputs

The current price of the standard cable crane equipment including cables is about £5,250, giving an hourly cost of £1·97.

Outputs vary over a fairly wide range but the following (Table 14.1) are taken from a fairly typical thinning extraction along racks spaced at 25 m.

TABLE 14.1

Max Rack Length, m	Output per hour in m³		
	Load size in m³		
	0·2	0·4	0·6
100	1·66	2·27	2·59
150	1·69	2·48	2·94
200	1·64	2·51	3·06
250	1·56	2·48	3·09
300	1·48	2·41	3·05

Terminal, movement and set-up and take-down times are included.

One of the major problems yet to be solved satisfactorily is the severe limitation of stacking space on mountain roads. Although more serious in clear felling it can still cause difficulty in thinning areas unless produce is removed rapidly from the end of the cable crane. In some circumstances it has been found advantageous to work with two sets of rigging and move the winch tractor to a fresh set-up whilst the previous set-up is being cleared.

Paper 15

MECHANIZED THINNING SYSTEMS

By C. J. BREDBERG

Royal College of Forestry, Department of Operational Efficiency, Garpenberg, Sweden

Only 20 years ago thinnings were the main source of wood in Sweden. Rapidly increasing costs for cutting small wood has made it necessary to reduce the amount of wood from thinnings and increase the clear-cutting. Today about 20 per cent of the total wood cut comes from thinnings. This development has been achieved by reducing the number of thinnings during the rotation and making the few remaining thinnings heavier. Similar changes can be noticed also in many other countries. As a matter of fact a large proportion of the increase in labour productivity during the last decades may be explained by the change-over to bigger trees. If this development continues we may have to manage our forests without thinning – one of our most

efficient tools to regulate the stand development towards the product wanted for clear-cuttings. If we consider that thinning is a necessary tool in the future development of stands, we have to develop new logging machines and systems especially designed for high productivity and low costs in small-wood.

Today the conventional logging system in Swedish thinnings is a short-wood system where the trees are felled, delimbed and bucked using a chain-saw. The logs are gathered in small piles at 4 metres wide strip-roads, spaced at 18–20 metres. The wood is then forwarded to the road-side by using small and medium sized rubber-tyred forwarders.

So, what are the features of this and similar motor-

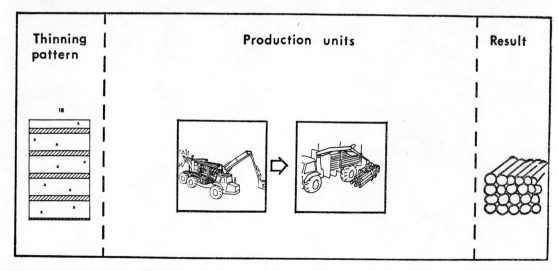

Figure 15.1 Motor-manual cutting.

manual systems that make them so unsuitable that they cannot survive in the future? First, the labour cost is as much as 70–80 per cent of the total cost which means that the cost will increase rapidly over time. By comparison, the labour cost in some mechanized systems is estimated at 20–30 per cent of the total. The motor-manual felling and processing of small trees in thinnings is not feasible under snow conditions. In such areas thinnings are made mainly during the bare-ground season. This in turn interferes with a peak in labour demand for other silvi-

cultural work. Furthermore, it is questionable if the motor-manual cutting can be accepted in the long run considering the poor ergonomical and environmental conditions.

The manual gathering of wood to strip-roads makes it necessary to keep the distance between the roads short. This in turn will reduce the selective part of the cutting and increase the strip-rack area (geometric) as well as the frequency of damage on remaining trees caused by the forwarders. A high road density also reduces the volume of harvested wood per unit of road length, causing an increase in the cost for subsequent terrain transportation.

It is probably impossible to find a solution that eliminates all these disadvantages. Lately, efforts have been made especially to reduce the damage from the forwarding operations. In this connection winching systems, e.g. the Radiotir-system (1) have been introduced.

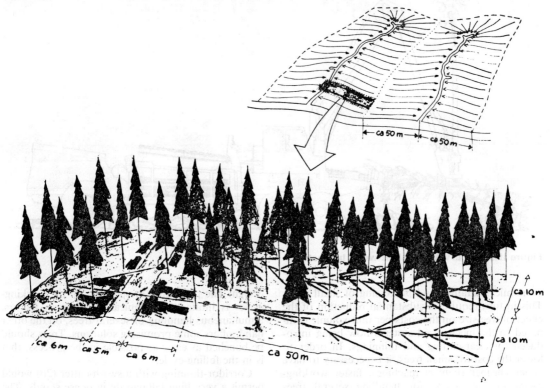

Figure 15.2 Principles of the winching methods (m = metres).

By winching the trees, the distance between the strip-roads may be increased to 80–100 metres. In the Radiotir system, the trees are felled towards the strip-road and delimbed by using a chain-saw. The stems are then pulled in bundles by a radiocontrolled, portable winch into the previously cut strip-road area, where they are bucked by means of a chainsaw. The conditions for forwarding are favourable because of the high concentration of wood along the roads. This winching system does not increase the labour-productivity, but makes the manual work less heavy and reduces the damage caused by the forwarder. However, it has been claimed that serious damage to the remaining trees appear also after winching.

Winching systems are now being further developed. More powerful tractor-mounted winches are being introduced. Some short-wood processors are being tried to work on the strip-roads. Whole-tree chipping has been tried in this connection as well. However, no near-future solutions are available for the mechanization of the motor-manual felling and the time-consuming winching.

Another thinning system being developed in Sweden is based on the LIVAB G1 short-wood harvester. This machine fells and extracts trees within the 10 metres reach of the boom. (See Figure 15.3).

The trees are automatically processed into 3-metre pulp-wood bolts and separated into two assortments. Sawlogs of varying lengths may also be produced. The machine is expected to harvest about 2 trees per minute. Since the felling-head handles one tree at a time only, the cost per cubic metre is heavily affected by tree size, as is the case for similar machines in clear-cuttings. This harvester, therefore, is primarily suited for later thinnings or clear-cuttings where trees are small enough. The LIVAB project has recently produced a second prototype (G2), substantially different from the one just shown.

Probably none of these systems being developed represent long-term solutions to the thinning problem. The mechanization of thinnings is a matter of

Figure 15.3 The LIVAB G1 short-wood harvester.

economical handling and processing of small trees. This in turn requires a substantial reduction of the effect of tree-size on the costs per unit volume compared to the mechanized systems now being introduced for clear-cutting and thinnings. In order to lower the cost for small trees, it is necessary to have either cheaper (lighter) machines, faster working-cycles or the facility for handling several trees simultaneously in each working-cycle.

In the long run, sticking to small and cheap machines will obstruct the application of modern technology in wood handling, processing and tractor design. The possibility of speeding up the working-cycles is limited by technical and human factors. Simultaneous handling of several trees, on the other hand, offers some promising solutions. Trees should be bunched as early as possible in the process, that is in the felling-cycle.

Corridor-thinning with a swath-cutter (2b) would permit a very high felling-rate in dense stands. The swath-cutter (Figure 15.4) covers a constant area per time unit independent of stand density and tree-size.

The basic concept is similar to that of a harvester

Figure 15.4 Hypothetical swath-cutter.

used in agriculture. Felling-rates of 5–10 trees per minute may be achieved this way. However, corridor-thinning seldom meets the silvicultural requirements concerning the spatial distribution of remaining trees. Often thinnings are not motivated unless the cutting is selective, favouring the best trees of the stand.

In selective thinnings, the mechanized felling of small trees may be speeded up by designing the felling-head so that it will manage to collect several

trees (2c) and swing them into the machine as a bundle rather than one tree at a time (See Figure 15.5).

The smaller the trees are, the shorter will be the felling time per tree, since a greater number of trees may be collected into the same bundle. This way the time per tree may be reduced by 30–40 per cent compared to the time taken using felling-heads that handle only one tree at a time (3).

The processing of small trees in bundles offers a

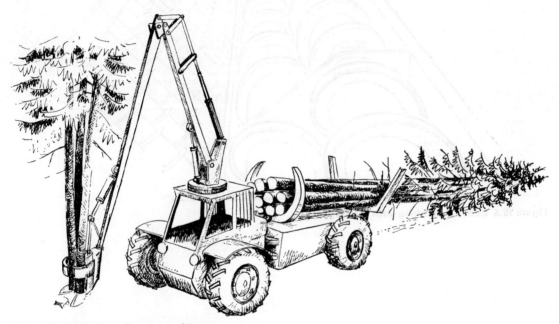

Figure 15.5 Feller handling several trees.

few different technical solutions (2c). In order to limit the size of a bunch-delimber, the bundles should first be cut to even lengths and then fed into the delimber. Trials have shown that the delimbing is unsatisfactory when the logs just wear against each other, e.g. by tumbling. Some kind of shearing tools has to be used. The "Kockum bunch-delimber" is one example, where rotating spiral-edged screws are used for the delimbing. (See Figure 15.6).

Other concepts of bunch delimbing that have been tried out experimentally are the drum-delimber (Figure 15.7) and the delimbing cradle (Figure 15.8). The delimbing is here made with the aid of knives mounted on the outside of the drum and between the cross-conveyors of the cradle. These delimbing methods are similar, but the cradle admits faster delimbing and a more simple feeding installation compared to the drum. Furthermore the construction of the cradle is less complicated.

The handling of several trees at a time in the felling, bucking and delimbing activities might be brought together in one machine – a bunch-delimbing harvester (See Figure 15.9).

The harvester accumulates trees in the felling-head. The tree-bundles are slashed and delimbed to pulp-wood bolts that are collected in a cradle at the rear of the machine. When the cradle is filled, it is emptied at the side of the strip-road, for subsequent transportation by a conventional forwarder.

Bunch-processing can also be achieved by chipping the trees with tops, branches and bark. However, chips in the woods, are a problem. Containers may be used, but then we create a "hot" system with strong demands on the planning and organisation of transportation. It can also be questioned if it is sensible to mix low quality chips from branches and tops with more valuable chips from the stem. Another alternative to achieve a more efficient use

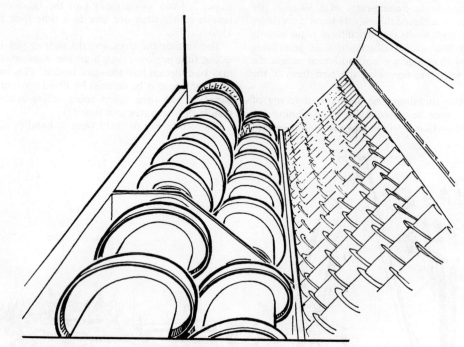

Figure 15.6 Bunch de-limbing with rotating screws.

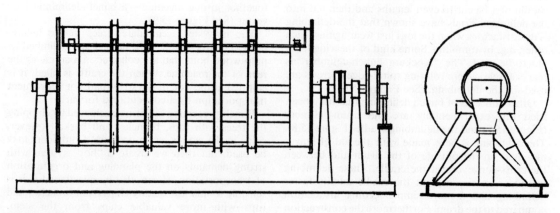

Figure 15.7 A set-up for de-limbing in a drum.

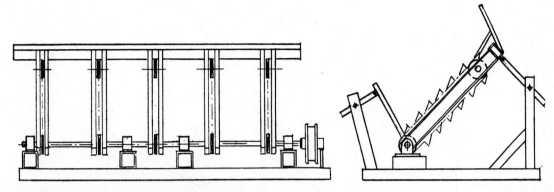

Figure 15.8 A set-up for de-limbing in a cradle.

Figure 15.9 Bunch-delimbing harvester.

of the tree would be a system which would separate the pulp-wood from branches and tops so that they could be used for different purposes. In order to facilitate the transportation of branches and tops to the mill for processing, they could be compressed to convenient-sized bales. Studies have shown that branches and tops may be compressed to a volume weight of 400–600 kilos per cubic metre. The volume weight of chips is in the order of 300 kilos per cubic metre.

Anyway, whole-tree utilization in thinning is certainly promising, considering that the merchantable part of the trunk accounts for only some 30–50 per cent of the total weight of a small tree. A con-

siderable increase in fibre-yield and revenues may therefore be expected.

I would like to summarize my view of the different concepts by a schematic comparison of the costs for harvesting and terrain transportation. (Figure 15.10). The comparison refers to early thinnings where the average DBH of thinned trees is about 10 cm. The cost forecast is based on the assumption that the labour cost per cubic metre increases twice as fast as the machine cost.

The graph may serve as an aid when discussing the expected development of logging systems for thinnings.

Obviously, the expected cost development of

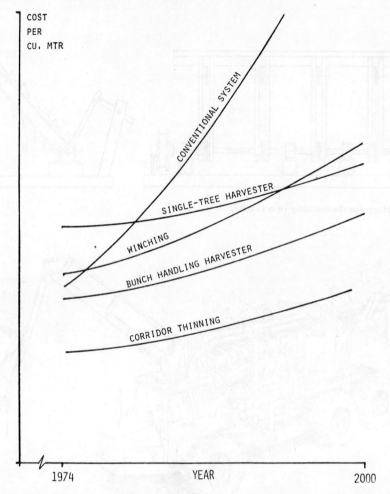

Figure 15.10 Schematic comparison of the cost of harvesting and terrain transportation.

today's thinning systems – short-wood or tree-length – will make the thinnings obsolete if we cannot find other solutions. The most serious obstacle in the mechanization of thinnings seems to be the damages on the stand caused primarily by the terrain-transportation vehicles. This may be solved by an expensive and time-consuming development of chassis, transmission and ground contacts (tyres, tracks etc). In the meantime winching-systems with wide road spacing offer solutions with varying degree of mechanization. The processing of bundles may also be employed in this connection. Hopefully, at the end of the 1980s the technology will allow fully mechanized systems with bunch-delimbing (or chip-

ping) harvesters and forwarders operating on closely spaced strip-roads. Looking still further into the future the swath-cutting of strip-roads or corridors offers a possibility for further increase in productivity.

Finally, it has to be emphasized that a development of this kind requires special efforts. If people involved in silviculture and logging don't start working seriously on technical solutions 10–15 years ahead, there will be no new machines on the market when we need them. Then we have sacrificed our possibilities to use thinning as an aid in forest management.

REFERENCES

(1) LARSSON, T. AND PERMALM, H. (1971). *Study of winching by the Radiotir System.* Logging Research Foundation. Report No. 7, 1971.

(2) *Thinning in the forestry of the future.* Reprint of papers from the international conference at ELMIA 1973. Dept. of oper. eff. Royal College of Forestry. Research Notes No. 69.

(2a) FRIES, J. *Thinning – why and how?*

(2b) BREDBERG, C-J. *Some mechanized thinning systems.*

(2c) MYHRMAN, D. *Techniques for mechanized thinning.*

(3) BREDBERG, C-J. AND MOBERG, L. (1972). *Felling heads designed for simultaneous handling of several trees.* Dept. of oper. eff. Royal College of Forestry. Research Notes No. 51.

DISCUSSION

Stratmann: I would expect that in thinning, tree felling by a machine is more costly than tree felling using a power saw. Did you find this in your studies?

Bredberg: I would guess that you are right if you are only considering the felling of the tree but when you take into account all other operations, extraction etc, the cost levels would be about the same.

Fries: I think it is quite important that in all these studies one should take account of as many factors as possible. That is, one should consider not merely the profitability but also the time consumed, the volume yielded and so on. The manager ought to have the complete details so that when prices etc change he is still in a good position to make a decision.

Jensen: It may be that we should also take into account when we are comparing machines with manual labour, the notion of a shadow price of manual labour and not the nominal price.

Rowan: Could Mr. Busby define the shadow price?

Busby: The shadow price is the resource cost of labour. For example, if forest workers could not find other employment then if they cease to work in forestry they would become unproductive and thus the social opportunity cost of continuing to employ them in forestry would be zero. In other words, the shadow price would be zero. Usually, however, at least a proportion of forest workers would be able to move from their present occupations to other occupations. By considering the overall re-employment position a weighted shadow price can be calculated.

GENERAL DISCUSSION ON PAPERS 11 - 15

Fox: Industry is seeking uniform material so that we have a trend towards uniformity. I would expect that the silvicultural system aiming at a uniform product would imply a short rotation.

Stratmann: I would say that in Germany we are tending to move from short rotations of about 60 years to longer rotations of about 120 years.

Busby: I think this is entirely due to the cost of capital. If you have zero cost of capital then you can reasonably have long rotations. The higher the cost of capital the shorter the optimum economic rotation length.

Forster: On this subject I think we could argue endlessly about rates of interest etc. As a researcher I think it is really important not only to outline in physical terms but also in economic terms all the consequences and all the logical alternatives, and then let the manager choose.

Fries: I agree with this. For example, many pulpwood companies claim that they are interested only in pulp and are not concerned about dimensions or saw timber quality, but in the event when they harvest timber you will frequently find they sell the saw timber element as saw timber and get useful revenues from that material. Therefore we should not always take the practitioners requirements at face value but should continue to consider the various alternative products in our research activities.

Young: In Maine we have a number of paper companies, none of which were connected with a saw-

mill, but in the last three years at least six of these have bought an existing sawmill or added a mill. I see a movement in the United States away from massive fibre production towards maximising the product and getting fibre from the residual material, that is the smaller trees. In Maine we are using Finland, Norway and Sweden as our models because they have been doing this for a long time.

Bredberg: In Sweden we try to maintain a management regime that gives us the greatest possible flexibility in the future. Turning towards short rotation forestry will not give us flexibility because it will consume a lot of the "storage" we have in terms of the growing stock. Once we find that we need to produce larger timber we would have to build up our storage once again, which would imply a serious reduction in harvesting for a considerable period. That is the situation we put ourselves in if we want to turn to short rotation forestry.

Sutton: I must protest against the idea that short rotations always imply low quality smallwood. The whole point of short rotations in New Zealand is to produce high quality sawnwood.

Rowan: I think underlying all the discussions today we see that research must be integrated research, so that all the people concerned, engineers, mensurationists, economists and industry are there to help us. I, as a manager, draw great comfort from the fact that no matter what decision I may come to I am certain to find some kind of authority among researchers somewhere for whatever course of action I choose to adopt.

Printed in England for Her Majesty's Stationery Office
by J. Looker, Ltd., 82 High Street, Poole, Dorset
Dd. 289242 K36 12/75